THE
SPORTS
PERFORMANCE
FACTORS

OTHER BOOKS BY THE AUTHORS

James M. Rippe, M.D.
Manual of Cardiovascular Diagnosis and Therapy
Manual of Intensive Care Medicine
Intensive Care Medicine
Fitness Walking

William Southmayd, M.D.
Sports Health

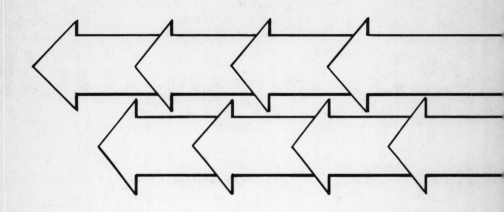

THE
SPORTS
PERFORMANCE
FACTORS

James M. Rippe, M.D.,
and
William Southmayd, M.D.

**with chapters on
training, and pain and
performance by Arthur Pappas, M.D.;
nutrition by Nancy Clark, M.S.; and
flexibility and mental strategies
by Jon Kabat-Zinn, Ph.D.**

A Perigee Book

Perigee Books
are published by
The Putnam Publishing Group
200 Madison Avenue
New York, NY 10016

The authors gratefully acknowledge
permission from *North News* to
reprint material from "The Psychology
of Winning" by John Bertrand,
from the Winter 1985 issue of
North News. Copyright © 1985 by
North Sails Inc.

All illustrations are by Joy D. Marllowe.

Typeset by Fisher Composition, Inc.

Library of Congress Cataloging-in-Publication Data

Rippe, James M.
The sports performance factors.

Includes index.
1. Sports—Physiological aspects.   2. Sports
medicine.   I. Southmayd, William.   II. Title.
RC1235.R57   1986   613'.0880796   86-4974
ISBN 0-399-51188-1

Printed in the United States of America
1   2   3   4   5   6   7   8   9   10

ACKNOWLEDGMENTS

Any book of this size must blend the efforts of many individuals. Many friends and colleagues have helped us in this effort and we are deeply grateful to them. Professor Patty Freedson provided valuable criticism of the entire manuscript and helpful advice on all the aerobic exercise prescriptions. Professor Kevin Campbell helped elucidate a number of issues in biomechanics. The staff of the Exercise Physiology Laboratory at the University of Massachusetts Medical School gave generously of their time and ideas. The staff of Sports Medicine Resources also helped in a variety of important ways.

Dr. Jessica Ross provided many helpful insights and helped manage a busy cardiology practice. Dr. Ann Ward helped clarify our thinking on the exercise physiology portions. Dr. Jon Kabat-Zinn contributed the material for the stretching routines throughout the book, in addition to his chapters on flexibility and mental strategies.

Our administrative staffs including Maryann Falvey, Beth Porcaro and Martine Paim helped organize our busy professional lives to create the time and space needed to complete the manuscript. Our friends and families offered invaluable support and encouragement to keep us going.

Finally, our editor, Adrienne Ingrum, championed this book from its earliest days and did a superb job in pulling the whole project together.

To these people, and to all the others who inspired and helped us along the way, our sincere thanks.

CONTENTS

INTRODUCTION

Performance. The athlete lives or dies by it. For the artist it is the final test. For the businessman it is the bottom line. In the final analysis we all care passionately about performance.

We all admire great performers—individuals who rise above the ordinary, whose lives and efforts inspire us and remind us of the greatness of the human spirit. Larry Bird sinking a 25-foot jump shot to win the game. Mary Lou Retton "sticking" a perfect 10 on her final vault to win Olympic Gold. Mikhail Baryshnikov soaring high through the air in an explosive leap. These great performers combine immense talent with years of dedication, unwavering concentration and competitive fires that cannot be extinguished. Performance is their life.

Yet performance is not important to just athletes or artists. Whether at work, during recreation or at leisure, we all strive to maximize our potential and improve our performance.

As physicians and health care providers, we have devoted our professional lives to helping others lead the healthiest, most productive lives possible. In the past twenty years incredible new information has become available uncovering the links between health, fitness and daily performance. This is information we use in our daily contacts with individuals seeking to improve their performance—whether they are professional athletes seeking better training regimens, recreational athletes seeking better conditioning or cardiac rehabilitation patients increasing their activity as they recover from a heart attack.

The purpose of this book is to assemble the information we use in our daily practices of cardiology, sports medicine and orthopedics. Many of the protocols, testing procedures and exercise prescriptions are ones developed at our Exercise Physiology Laboratory at the University of Massachusetts Medical School in Worcester, Massachusetts, and at Sports

Medicine Resources, our sports medicine clinic in Brookline, Massachusetts. They represent our experience with thousands of athletes and patients over the past fifteen years.

We have organized this book with two goals in mind: first, to help you plan and carry out a comprehensive program to enhance your own human performance; second, to summarize recent advances in knowledge about human performance and to apply this knowledge specifically to sports performance. We provide our 7 Building Blocks framework for a program of health and fitness and a series of tests to determine your fitness level. You can develop your own health and fitness program, with specific prescriptions based on your test scores. Chapters 2–8 look at each of the 7 Building Blocks separately.

How should you use this book?

Read chapter 1 for a general overview to the self-tests. Once you have tested yourself, start on the action plans in chapter 2 for your own program of health and fitness. Chapters 3–8 can serve as background reading on each of the 7 Building Blocks, clarifying points and illuminating your own experience. Chapters 9 and 10 provide strategies to reduce risk factors for heart disease and adopt positive lifestyle behaviors.

1

Health, Fitness and Performance

In the past decade we have witnessed a revolution in the way Americans think and act about exercise. On any given day, up to 50% of adults slip out of their work clothes and into athletic gear. Over 70% of these individuals exercise at least once a week. Pollster George Gallup surveyed this trend and called it the most important social phenomenon he had observed in a lifetime of assessing American attitudes.

People exercise for a variety of reasons. Some to lose weight, others because they think it makes them look better, feel more relaxed or have more energy. But the number-one reason is for *health*.

As physicians we are encouraged by the tremendous upsurge in interest in health and fitness in the past decade. Much of the information in this book has come to light recently as more physicians and exercise physiologists focus attention on the relationship between health and fitness.

The best approach to total health and fitness involves more than just one discipline. This is what brought the authors together. Dr. Southmayd set up a sports medicine clinic with the concept of providing the best treatment and rehabilitation to athletes, either professional or recreational. Over the past ten years, this facility has grown into the largest sports medicine clinic in New England with over 18,000 patient visits a year. Dr. Rippe ran the largest cardiac rehabilitation program in New England and serves as the medical director of a medical school exercise physiology laboratory. While one of us approached the topic from the aspect of musculoskeletal fitness and the other from the effects of exercise on the heart, we shared a common final goal.

Some of the early advocates of fitness in our society focused too much on aerobic exercise alone. They tended to overemphasize the isolated role of exercise in contributing to good health. Now we recognize the need for a comprehensive approach. The "7 Building Blocks" for total fitness is our attempt to provide a *simple* yet comprehensive approach to health and fitness that all people can understand and adapt to their lifestyle.

A total fitness program must have a balance among many different factors. *Aerobic conditioning* forms the core of our program. *Flexibility* is important, and a program of stretching and flexibility exercises is an essential part of total fitness. *Strength*, power and muscular endurance; *mental strategies; proper nutrition;* and *training* techniques are also important. All together, these building blocks will maximize your overall *performance*.

Not long ago we had the opportunity to share our 7 Building Blocks concept with the 300 top salespeople from a high-tech company. At the end of our presentation one of the salesmen asked whether most physicians shared our philosophy that health and fitness were closely related. He said that in all the years he had been going to his physician for annual physical examinations he had never once been questioned or advised about his nutritional habits or level of exercise.

We had to admit that many of our colleagues still do not share our commitment to total fitness. But from our travels around the country we have been struck by the tremendous increase in interest among physicians in learning about exercise and fitness prescription.

That the medical profession has been slow to respond to the fitness needs of the population has been less of a problem than the horde of individuals who have rushed in to fill the vacuum. To some degree the rapid growth of interest in fitness has turned it into a fad in our country. As a result, many entrepreneurs have gravitated to the area. We have individuals who are not nutritionists offering advice on nutrition, movie stars offering advice on exercise and flexibility, and television personalities conducting workout sessions. Most of these individuals may be well intentioned and may be making a positive contribution, but there is an urgent need to offer sound medical advice in health and fitness.

Just in the past year we have seen a dramatic rise in joint and muscle injuries from participants in aerobic dance classes, some of whom may have failed to warm up properly. An increasing number of injuries occur when individuals load weight onto their arms or legs while exercising. The shin splints, muscle pulls, knee problems and overuse injuries from overzealous runners continue to support a number of sports medicine clinics around the country.

What is urgently needed is a straightforward, specific and medically sound approach to the prescription of exercise and other aspects of total fitness. We hope this book begins this process. Take it with you to your next doctor's appointment. We think you will find that your physician will support your efforts to improve your health and fitness and will be able to make some suggestions to help tailor a program specifically for you.

One final word of advice. If you have not paid enough attention to your personal fitness over the years, the time to start the cycle around is now. Remember, however, that it may have taken you years to drift into sedentary, stressful or high-risk patterns. It is going to take some time to turn things around.

If you carefully follow the step-by-step plans in this book, you will lessen your chance of suffering an early injury or facing early discouragement. Remember, to achieve the most important health benefits a fitness program must be lifelong, consistent and comprehensive. We will give you the right information. You must supply the discipline and common sense to put these plans into action.

HEALTH, FITNESS AND PERFORMANCE: THE LINKAGE

Two recent surveys (The Miller Lite Report on Sports and The American Health Survey on Fitness) asked Americans why they exercised. In both surveys more than 50% of respondents said that they exercised to improve their health.

Does exercise really improve your health? The answer is a resounding yes! But let's not congratulate ourselves too quickly about how the fitness movement is improving the health of Americans. Scratch the surface of the statement "I exercise for health" and you will find that most people have only vague impressions about how exercise is linked to good health and what they need to do to maximize the health benefits of their exercise programs.

For example, most people don't understand that the major benefits of exercise are the result of a lifelong, consistent exercise program. Studies have shown that college or even Olympic athletes who stop exercising once their competitive careers are over quickly revert to the same risk of developing heart disease as if they had never exercised at all. Of course, you get some short-term benefits from starting an exercise program, but the most important benefits—decreasing the likelihood of heart disease, maintaining musculoskeletal strength and endurance, slowing bone loss—belong to individuals who participate in lifelong, consistent exercise programs.

Let us give you another example. We were deeply saddened by the untimely death of author Jim Fixx. Yet perhaps some good will come out of this tragedy, because it focused national attention on putting exercise in a proper perspective. Some of the initial reactions to Mr. Fixx's death were truly astounding. Some people drew the conclusion that they should not exercise because, after all, it hadn't saved Jim Fixx!

These people obviously hadn't heard about the concept of risk factors. Scientific and medical studies over the past two decades have established the factors that put you at higher risk for developing heart disease: elevated blood cholesterol, high blood pressure, cigarette smoking, obesity, a sedentary lifestyle, a family history of premature heart disease, stress and diabetes.

To draw the conclusion that Mr. Fixx's devotion to exercise failed to prevent the development of a fatal heart attack vastly oversimplifies a complex problem. He had a family history of premature heart disease and had been a heavy cigarette smoker, sedentary and overweight earlier in his life. Mr. Fixx's exercise undoubtedly *was* good for him. But exercise alone is not a cure-all. You must combine it with an overall approach to risk factor reduction, proper nutrition and other fitness factors. We will give you the information you need to make the proper choices.

Is fitness linked to improved performance?

Yes! A recent survey of the health and fitness practices of chief executive officers and upper-level managers in Fortune 500 companies found that the individuals at the very top of their profession were leaner and more fit, and devoted more time to fitness than individuals lower on the corporate ladder.

Over 50,000 companies in the United States have initiated corporate fitness programs and over 400 of these are so committed that they have hired full-time fitness directors.

We recently asked some top businessmen to relate their level of fitness to their work habits and productivity. What we found was that individuals who had definite fitness plans felt happier and more productive at work and were significantly less likely to rate their jobs as stressful.

How did they find time for consistent fitness programs? They *made* time. In fact, the higher the number of hours worked per week, the more likely the individual was to have a consistent and highly planned fitness program. As one respondent commented, "I couldn't possibly work as hard as I do, if I didn't have a solid fitness program."

EXERCISE AND THE HEART

Most people who exercise for improved health have the sense that they are doing something good for their heart.

Is exercise really good for the heart? Yes. The effects of exercise on the heart are best understood by dividing them up into short- and long-term effects.

Short-Term Effects
of Exercise on The Heart

As soon as you take your first jogging step, make the first pedal revolution on your bicycle or stationary cycle or make your first dance step in aerobics class, the exercising muscles begin to burn energy and call on the heart and lungs to deliver more oxygen-rich blood. The heart and lungs cannot respond instantaneously and so for the first 45–90 seconds, the muscles rely largely on energy stores located in the muscles themselves. This whole process is depicted in fig. 1.

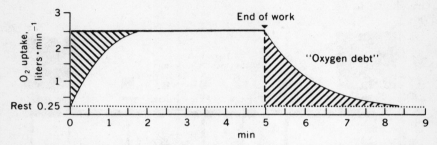

FIG. 1. During the first 45–90 seconds of exercise, the oxygen consumption rises until it reaches a steady state. From P. O. Åstrand and K. Rodahl, *Textbook of Work Physiology* (New York: McGraw-Hill, 1977), with permission.

During that first 45–90 seconds there is a gradual shift from making energy without oxygen, anaerobic metabolism, to the much more efficient process of making energy with oxygen, aerobic metabolism. Once the heart and lungs have responded, a steady state is achieved during which you burn the energy necessary to fill the demand. When you stop exercising, there is a period of increased metabolism. The exact reasons for this increased metabolism are still being debated, but restoring muscle energy stores appears to be a part of the process.

Fig. 1 depicts a number of experiences that athletes commonly undergo. First, it shows why it is important to warm up and cool down slowly. It takes your heart and lungs a period of time to adjust to exercise, so it is important to build up the pace gradually. Sudden strenuous exercise can put undue strain on the heart. Also, the body needs some time to burn off waste products accumulated during exercise, so it is important to taper off gradually at the end of a workout rather than just stop abruptly. This tapering-off period will also promote a faster recovery time for another bout of exercise.

The processes represented in fig. 1 also offer a partial explanation for the common experience of shortness of breath for the first minute or two when starting exercise. This is the time when the lungs are adjusting to the increased workload and beginning to clear some of the waste products from exercise. Finally, the response to exercise depicted in fig. 1 gives a partial answer for why many top athletes regard the 440-yard run or 100-yard swim as the most strenuous athletic events. Each of these events takes top competitors 45 to 60 seconds to complete—thus stressing the body's energy-burning processes to the maximum without ever allowing the heart and lungs to reach a steady state.

During exercise, dramatic changes can occur in the blood flow in order to meet the needs of the exercising muscles, as well as maintain the vital functions of the brain, heart and other vital organs. These changes are shown in fig. 2.

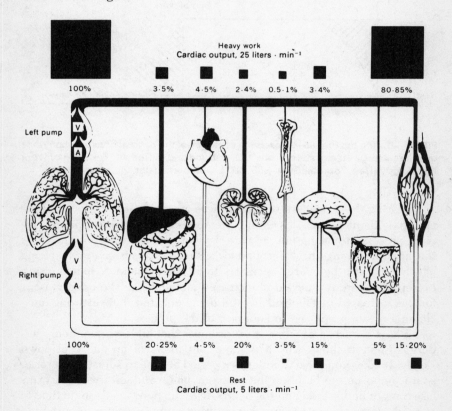

FIG. 2. As shown in this figure, during vigorous exercise the cardiac output (amount of blood pumped by the heart) may increase to five or six times what it is at rest. The blood flow distribution also changes so that more blood goes to the exercising muscles. From Åstrand and Rodahl, *Textbook of Work Physiology*, with permission.

The first aspect of exercise shown in fig. 2 is that the total amount of blood pumped out by the heart (the cardiac output) rises significantly during exercise. A well-conditioned individual can increase this blood flow to five or six times what it is at rest. Second, the body has a magnificent system for distributing blood flow to the areas where it is needed. Blood flow to the legs during running can increase by as much as thirty times over that during rest!

When you begin an exercise program, a number of changes occur over the first few weeks and months to make the whole energy-burning system work more efficiently. The heart size increases slightly, thus allowing more blood to be pumped out per beat. Since the heart now pumps more blood per beat, the resting heart rate can decrease. The muscles also become much more efficient. This enables them to pull increased amounts of oxygen out of the blood and allows more energy to be burned with less strain on the heart. The combination of these changes is known as the "training effect." What an individual typically notices is that his or her resting heart rate is decreased. The ability to perform tasks with less fatigue and an overall sense of increased energy may also accompany the training effect.

Long-Term Benefits of Exercise on the Heart

There are a number of important long-term benefits of consistent, aerobic exercise, provided that it is carried out throughout a lifetime. Most of these benefits revolve around the role of exercise in preventing coronary artery disease (the disease that causes heart attacks and angina). Lately considerable attention has been focused on the debate about whether or not exercise prevents heart disease. Those people who argue that exercise does not prevent heart disease either point out the death of some prominent exercise proponent such as Jim Fixx or maintain that the evidence favoring the preventative benefits of exercise is not entirely conclusive. We agree. However, so much evidence links consistent, lifelong exercise to prevention of heart disease that there is no need to wait for 100 percent proof. We put individuals on exercise programs because we are certain that the programs improve people's health—in both the short term and the long term.

Two scientific studies done by Dr. Ralph Paffenbarger followed a number of individuals for extended periods of time to assess how their physical activity related to the likelihood of developing heart disease. One study was conducted in the workplace and the other looked at leisure-time activities. Both found the identical result—increased activity or exercise dramatically *decreased* the chance of heart attack.

The workplace study was conducted among longshoremen in San Francisco. The longshoremen whose jobs required consistent heavy exertion suffered significantly fewer heart attacks than did individuals with jobs classified as light exertion or sedentary.

The leisure-activity study looked at over 16,000 Harvard graduates and followed them over a 16-year period. The most important finding from this study is shown in fig. 3.

What the study found was that even small amounts of exercise (such as walking five city blocks or climbing five flights of stairs) performed on a daily basis significantly decreased the likelihood of heart attack. As shown in fig. 3, even an hour of vigorous exercise a week resulted in a significant decline in heart disease and the benefits continued to accrue sharply up to 4–5 hours of vigorous exercise per week.

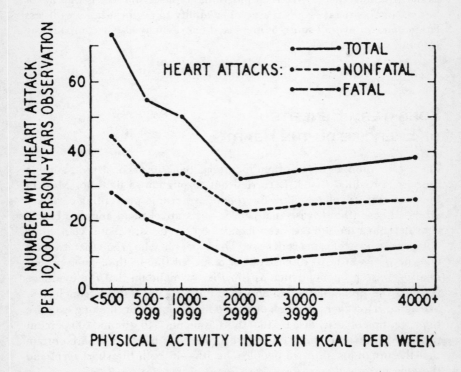

FIG. 3.   Data from over 16,000 college graduates followed over a sixteen-year period. Individuals who exercised regularly were significantly less likely to develop a heart attack than those who did not. From R. S. Paffenbarger, A. L. Wing, and R. T. Hyde, "Physical Activity as an Index of Heart Risk in College Alumni." *American Journal of Epidemiology* 108 (1978): 161, with permission.

OTHER HEALTH BENEFITS OF EXERCISE

- Prevention of obesity: Over half of the American adult population is overweight. Exercise is one of the parts of a weight-loss program that has been shown consistently effective. We are skeptical about any weight-loss program that doesn't include an exercise component. Even more important, exercise is absolutely essential for losing the kind of weight you want to. Exercise helps preserve lean body weight while you lose *fat*.
- Mental health: Many avid exercisers praise the mental benefits they achieve from exercise. These include relief of stress, increased awareness, increased calmness and mental energy. The exact basis of these benefits remains unclear, but they are commonly experienced.
- Slowing of bone loss: Some studies suggest that exercise may be very helpful in slowing the bone loss (osteoporosis) which may accompany aging, particularly in females.
- Musculoskeletal fitness: Exercise strengthens tendons, ligaments and cartilage. This decreases your likelihood of muscles or joint injury during physical work or recreation.
- Diabetes: Exercise helps the muscles take up sugar from the blood. This can often reduce the amount of insulin required by an individual with diabetes.

STARTING YOUR OWN
PROGRAM OF TOTAL FITNESS

Science and medicine have made great advances in the past decade to help you plan a comprehensive program. What it takes on your part is work and discipline to put a total fitness program into place. Changing unhealthy patterns that may have taken years to develop takes motivation. While we have focused considerable attention on exercise, remember that this is only part of the picture. By following our 7 Building Blocks system you can build a program to put you on the path toward total fitness.

THE 7 BUILDING BLOCKS

The 7 Building Blocks—aerobic conditioning, flexibility, strength training, mental strategies, nutrition, training and performance—represent a formidable structure to build your health and fitness program. If you disregard any one of them, however, you substantially weaken the effectiveness of this total program for health and fitness.

1. AEROBIC CONDITIONING

The word *aerobic* means "in the presence of oxygen." Aerobic conditioning is the process of putting stress on the systems that deliver oxygen to exercising muscles so that these become stronger and more efficient. As you sit reading this book your aerobic system is quietly functioning, burning the fuel you need to maintain your normal bodily functions. The system for burning energy is divided into two major subsystems: the aerobic and the anaerobic. The aerobic subsystem is designed to allow you to perform long periods of endurance activities. The anaerobic subsystem (sort of a booster pump) provides much of the energy for the initial minute of exercise and short bursts of intense activity.

In practice, all exercise is partially aerobic and partially anaerobic. However, certain sports, among them walking, jogging, running, cycling, stationary cycling and swimming, that use the large muscle groups in a repetitive fashion are particularly effective for training the heart and other muscles. These are the aerobic sports we recommend as the core of your personal fitness program.

2. FLEXIBILITY

Far too few people pay adequate attention to flexibility and stretching. We are firm believers in stretching and other flexibility measures and recommend that our patients perform them both before *and* after exercise. The periods immediately before exercise (the warm-up period) and immediately following exercise (the cool-down period) are critical times in the safe performance of exercise and the implementation of a total fitness program. When we speak about flexibility we are talking not just about stretching but also about proper warming-up and cooling-down techniques, breathing and mental preparation.

Stretching nourishes the muscles, and proper stretching techniques can enhance muscular performance. Improved flexibility involves techniques for breathing, mental preparation, proper warm-up and cooldown. You will learn about all of these factors as well as proper stretching in the chapter on flexibility, written by our colleague, Dr. Jon Kabat-Zinn, an expert in the use of stretching to increase musculoskeletal fitness and performance.

3. STRENGTH TRAINING

Modern strength, power and muscular endurance training techniques can improve both strength and speed. Combined with a proper stretching program, flexibility need not suffer. Strength and power programs have proved so effective that it is very common for professional athletes and top amateurs to have a strength training program. Even athletes in such sports as golf and tennis have benefited from properly designed musculoskeletal strength programs.

Strength measures the ability to overcome resistance. Thus, an individual who can lift 200 pounds is stronger than an individual who can lift only 100 pounds. *Power* is the combination of strength and speed. Clearly for most athletes power is much more important than just strength. *Muscular endurance* is a measure of how many repetitions a muscle can perform before fatiguing.

4. MENTAL STRATEGIES

The importance of mental conditioning in high-level athletic competition leaped into the national consciousness during the 1984 Summer and Winter Olympic games. There, many people saw for the first time the intense mental preparation that accompanies high-level sports. Many American athletes are involved in visualization practices in which they concentrate on images or play the contest or event over and over again in their "mind's eye" and visualize themselves performing flawlessly. Other athletes now routinely travel with their own sports psychologist to help them develop and rehearse effective mental strategies. These practices, which are just now being introduced in American sport, have long been mainstays of Eastern European athletes. It has become well recognized that human performance at any level depends to a great extent on mental factors and that these can be optimized by systematic training in techniques such as meditation, relaxation and mental rehearsal.

5. NUTRITION

The best diet is one that supplies all the essential nutrients to allow tissue maintenance, growth and repair. It would seem that this would lead to simple recommendations for most adults. However, it is complicated by the fact that different individuals have different levels of activity, different body sizes, different digestive patterns and different metabolic rates. The matter may be further complicated for the athlete or individual involved in a consistent exercise program. While considerable research has been done on this last subject, the consensus is that athletes do *not* require nutrients beyond those derived from a balanced diet. *In essence, sound nutrition for the athlete or individual involved in serious daily exercise is sound human nutrition.*

For most people, decreases in the amount of fats and protein with a corresponding increase in the amount of complex carbohydrates would be the best modifications. This is particularly true if you increase your level of exercise.

Balanced nutrition and a sensible approach to nutrition for weight loss are just two of many important aspects of nutrition which you will learn about in this book. Nancy Clark, director of nutrition at Sports Medicine Resources, has contributed the chapter on nutrition.

6. TRAINING

The advent of interval training and of specialized muscular strength and power training programs, as well as a firmer grasp of the physiology of exercise, have contributed to the amazing and relentless onslaught on the record books.

Many of the advanced training techniques employed by professional and Olympic athletes are applicable also to the recreational athlete. Whether your desire is to have more energy for the third set of a tennis match, improve your time in 10-kilometer road races or just enjoy your leisure and recreational activities more, sound advice on training will be important to you. Specific training techniques can increase the safety of exercise for you as well as enhance your performance.

As training techniques have been refined, several important principles have emerged. First is the principle of *specificity:* Training is very specific for the activity performed. The second principle is *overload:* Aerobic capacity, power, endurance, flexibility and even mental concentration will grow and develop only if your training regimen is designed to stretch them beyond their initial capacity.

7. PERFORMANCE

Performance puts it all together. Top performance may mean very different things to different people. To some people, achieving an athletic goal such as improving running time, golf score or tennis performance will assume top priority. Other people will focus on improved levels of overall fitness while still others will want to focus most attention on enhancing their enjoyment of recreation or adding more energy in their day-to-day activities.

TESTING YOURSELF
FOR SPORTS PERFORMANCE

Before you begin the Sports Performance action plans found in the next chapter you should undergo a series of simple tests. These tests will establish baseline values for you and show you areas that need improvement. The tests will also provide you with the information you need to choose your specific plan of action.

SAFETY FIRST: THE PRE-PROGRAM EVALUATION

It is very important that you consult your physician prior to starting any new exercise program. If you have not received regular medical care or have not undergone a physical examination in the past year, make an appointment to see your doctor.

Your physician will want to discuss with you any risk factors you have for coronary artery disease (such as high blood pressure, an elevated cholesterol level, cigarette smoking, heart disease in your family). He or she will also perform a physical examination and obtain an electrocardiogram (EKG) and may also recommend an exercise tolerance test (ETT).

THE EXERCISE TOLERANCE TEST

The exercise tolerance test helps determine whether or not it is safe for you to start an exercise program. You will be asked to walk and then run at ever-increasing speeds and grades on a motorized treadmill.

We believe that any male who has been inactive for over a year and is over the age of 35 who wishes to start an exercise program ought to have this test. The same is true for any female over the age of 40 who has been inactive for over a year, and for previously sedentary individuals.

If you do have an exercise tolerance test, in addition to the information that your doctor receives, there are several pieces of information you will need from this test to determine your aerobic capacity. Be sure to ask your doctor for the following information:

Was the test performed using the Bruce protocol? There are a number of different treadmill test protocols. Over 90% of hospitals, however, use the Bruce protocol, so that is the one we have incorporated in our tests of aerobic capacity. If the test was *not* done using the Bruce protocol, you cannot use the information from the test to estimate your aerobic capacity in the next section.

The second piece of information you need to know is how many minutes you exercised on the treadmill. Ask your physician to give you the number of minutes and seconds you lasted on the treadmill.

THE TESTS OF HUMAN PERFORMANCE

We will test you in the following areas:

1. Aerobic capacity
2. Flexibility
3. Muscle strength and endurance
4. Body fat
5. Mental balance
6. Cardiac risk factors
7. Positive lifestyle

1. AEROBIC CAPACITY

We give you four methods for estimating your aerobic capacity. They are listed in rank order from the least accurate to the most accurate. Each of the four methods will lead you to a specific aerobic action plan designed to build on your current level of aerobic conditioning. Each method will also give you a score to plug into your Sports Performance Score.

Method 1: Estimated Activity Level

This is the least accurate method but it will give you a rough idea of your current level of aerobic conditioning. Rate your current level of physical activity according to following categories.

1. Inactive: You have a sit-down job and no regular physical activity.
2. Relatively inactive: Three to four hours per day of walking or standing are usual. You have no regular organized physical activity during leisure time.
3. Light physical activity: You are sporadically involved in recreational activities such as weekend golf or tennis, occasional jogging, swimming or cycling.
4. Moderate physical activity: Usual job activities might include climbing stairs or lifting, or you participate regularly in recreational/fitness activities such as jogging, swimming or cycling at least three times a week for 30 to 60 minutes each time.
5. Very vigorous physical activity: You participate in extensive physical activity for 60 minutes or more at least four days per week.

Aerobic Fitness Level Based on Estimated Activity Level

ACTIVITY LEVEL	FITNESS LEVEL
Inactive	Poor
Relatively inactive	Fair
Light physical activity	Average
Moderate physical activity	Good
Very vigorous physical activity	Excellent

Method 2: The Step Test

This method requires your active participation in a three-minute step test. It requires that you first learn how to take your pulse accurately. Every serious exerciser needs to learn how to do this anyway, so if you don't know how to take your pulse here's the technique we recommend: Jog in place for 30 seconds, then place your fingers on your wrist, throat or temple or directly over your heart.

If you use your wrist, place your fingers gently over the radial artery just inside the wrist bone. If you have trouble finding your pulse, try inserting your fingers softly into your neck at the Adam's apple just below your jaw. Don't press too hard, for this can slow your heart rate and you'll get an inaccurate reading. A third method is to press lightly with the fingers on your temple. You should have no problem finding your pulse at one of these locations or directly over your heart.

Take a few practice readings when you are rested and relaxed. All you need is a clock with a second hand. You'll get a general idea of your resting heart rate if you count your pulse for 30 seconds and multiply by two to determine the rate per minute. For most people, the resting pulse rate falls between 50 and 90 beats a minute.

The description of the Step Test is reprinted with minor changes from *Fitness Walking,* by Robert Sweetgall with James Rippe and Frank Katch (New York: Perigee, 1985).

The step test is an excellent, research-proven means for testing your heart's response to exercise. It is quick, and it is easy.

Suppose, for example, that three people perform three minutes of stepping up and down on a bench. Fig. 4 illustrates the heart rate response of each subject during the three minutes of stepping. During the first minute, the heart rate increases rapidly and then starts to level off. Subject A, a marathoner, reaches a heart rate of 120 beats per minute at the end of three minutes, while the heart rate of subject B, a housewife who exercises regularly, is 142 beats per minute. For subject C, a sedentary executive, the heart's response to the metabolic demands of this exercise is 170 beats per minute.

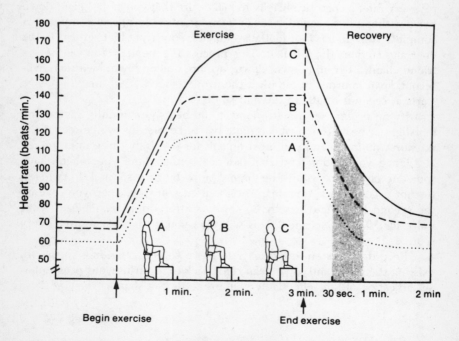

FIG. 4.   The heart rate response during exercise and recovery of three individuals with different fitness levels. From W. D. McArdle, F. I. Katch, and V. L. Katch, *Exercise Physiology.* (Philadelphia: Lea & Febiger, 1981), with permission.

It is clear that the cardiovascular stress of bench stepping for C is considerably greater than for the other two, especially A, whose increase in heart rate is minimal. It would be reasonable to conclude that cardiovascular capacity is greatest for the athlete, less for the housewife, and relatively poor for the sedentary business executive.

Fig. 4 also shows the pattern of heart rate recovery in the three subjects for two minutes immediately following the stepping exercise. Notice that on completion of the exercise, the heart rate decreases rapidly during the first 60 seconds of recovery. Following this period, the heart rate declines, but at a much slower pace. After two minutes, the heart rate essentially has returned to a resting state.

The noticeable differences in the recovery heart rates of these three people are observed during the first minute following exercise. This is a good way to judge how well your circulatory system responds to exercise.

The test can be performed alone, but it is much easier if you have a helper. Find a stair or stool eight inches high. (You can adjust the height with boards or phone books.) You are going to step onto this height, one foot after the other, up and down, for three minutes.

The correct stepping cadence is important in determining your heart recovery rate, so practice briefly to make sure that you step up and down twice within a five-second span, or 24 complete step-ups each minute. A complete step-up has four footfalls—that is, your right foot returns to the floor and so does the left foot. This process is repeated. You can have a friend chant, "Up, up; down, down; up, up; down, down," within a five-second span in order to establish the proper speed. Each new sequence starts at seconds 5, 10, 15, 20 and so on.

If you prefer, set a metronome to 96 beats per minute, giving one footstep per beat. You must complete two full cycles every five seconds— *no more, no less*—and you must do this for precisely three minutes.

Once you understand the cadence, either time yourself or have someone else signal you to begin and stop. Be precise, and do the step test for exactly three minutes. The moment you stop, keep your eye on the second hand, and exactly 30 seconds after stopping, measure your pulse for 30 more seconds. This will give you your heart rate recovery score.

Record your step-test heart rate score so you can compare it with existing standards and so you can refer back to it during your program as an indication of how effectively you are getting in shape.

**Aerobic Fitness Level Based on
30-Second Recovery Heart Rate for Men and Women***

Classification	Age			
	20–29	30–39	40–49	50 and older
Men		Number of Beats		
Excellent	34–36	35–38	37–39	37–40
Good	37–40	39–41	40–42	41–43
Average	41–42	42–43	43–44	44–45
Fair	43–47	44–47	45–49	46–49
Poor	48–59	48–59	50–60	50–62
Women				
Excellent	39–42	39–42	41–43	41–44
Good	43–44	43–45	44–45	45–47
Average	45–46	46–47	46–47	48–49
Fair	47–52	48–53	48–54	50–55
Poor	53–66	54–66	55–67	56–66

*Thirty-second recovery heart rate, the number of beats counted in 30 seconds, is measured beginning 30 seconds after exercise stops.

Adapted from and based on information in J. J. Montoye, *Physical Activity and Health: An Epidemiologic Study of an Entire Community* (Englewood Cliffs, NJ: Prentice-Hall, 1975).

Method 3: The 1.5-Mile Run

Our third test for estimating aerobic capacity is the 1.5-mile run. This test was developed and validated by Dr. Bruno Balke. It is a very vigorous test and we do not recommend it for individuals who have been very inactive or for men over the age of 35 or women over the age of 40 who are just starting an aerobic fitness program. (These individuals should have a monitored exercise tolerance test—see Method 4.)

The Balke 1.5-mile run is best performed on a measured track. Most high schools and colleges in your area will have outdoor quarter-mile tracks, and these are excellent for the 1.5-mile run. You should wear appropriate running clothes and shoes. Don't perform the test on a day where the ambient temperature is over 80° Fahrenheit, since this will add a significant heat load. After proper warm-up and stretching, begin the 1.5-mile run. The most common error in this run is to start out too fast, so take the first half mile easy. Try to establish a steady pace that you can run the entire distance. You can either time yourself or have a friend time you. Record your time for the run in minutes and seconds.

Estimating Aerobic Fitness Level
Based on Time to Complete 1.5-Mile Run

TIME (min:sec)	FITNESS LEVEL
12:00 or less	Excellent
12:01–14:59	Good
15:00–18:45	Average
18:46–22:29	Fair
22:30 or more	Poor

Method 4: The Exercise Tolerance Test

If you have undergone an exercise tolerance test on the treadmill (we recommend this test for males over 35, females over 40 and all previously sedentary individuals), merely record the number of minutes and seconds that you lasted on the treadmill.

Remember, the test must have been done with the Bruce protocol in order to generate a valid number to employ the categories below.

Estimating Aerobic Fitness Level Based on the Time Exercised
on an Exercise Tolerance Test on the Treadmill

TIME (min:sec)	FITNESS LEVEL
12:45 or more	Excellent
11:00–12:44	Good
8:20–10:59	Average
4:00–8:19	Fair
4:00 or less	Poor

Turn to p. 44 to score your fitness level determined through one of the four methods given above.

2. FLEXIBILITY

Test yourself when you are loosest, probably in the late afternoon or early evening. Do the nine stretches illustrated on pp. 33–35 as best you can and record your score for each one. The stippled areas on the figures show the major regions being tested in each case.

FIG. 5   FIG. 6   FIG. 7   FIG. 8

		Score
1. Standing toe-touch with knees locked. (Fig. 5)	Palms flat on the floor	20
	Fingertips touching toes	15
	Fingertips between ankles and knees	10
	Fingertips at or above knees	5

		Score
2. Standing back bend with arms over head. Stand 8 feet from a wall 8 feet high. (Fig. 6)	Can see wall directly behind you	10
	Can see where wall and ceiling meet behind you	7
	Can see only ceiling behind you	5
	Can see only ceiling above you	1

		Score
3. Standing side bend, feet 1 foot apart, arms parallel above head. Do in front of mirror. (Fig. 7)	90° bend—rib cage touches pelvis	10
	60° bend	7
	45° bend	5
	30° bend or less	1

		Score
4. Sitting, bend forward over outstretched leg. (Fig. 8)	Head can go to floor on inside of knee	10
	Head touches knee	7
	Head within 6 inches of knee	5
	Head more than 6 inches from knee	1

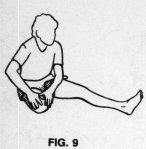

FIG. 9

FIG. 10

FIG. 11

FIG. 12

		Score
5. Sitting, put ankle on opposite thigh. (Fig. 9)	Knee touches floor unassisted	10
	Knee touches floor with pressure from hands	7
	Knee 1–4 inches above floor	5
	Knee more than 4 inches from floor	1

		Score
6. Plough, knees straight. (Fig. 10)	Toes touch floor	10
	Toes 1–6 inches from floor	7
	Toes 6–12 inches from floor	5
	Toes more than 12 inches from floor	1

		Score
7. Lying on belly, heel in buttock, lift knee. (Fig. 11)	Heel in buttock, knee more than 3 inches off floor	10
	Heel in buttock, knee 1–2 inches off floor	7
	Heel in buttock, cannot lift knee	5
	Heel will not go to buttock	1

		Score
8. Cow's-head pose. (Fig. 12)	Can grasp fingers easily	10
	Can grasp fingers barely	7
	Can touch fingertips	5
	Cannot touch fingertips	1

FIG. 13

FIG. 14

		Score
9. Spinal twist. (Fig. 13)	Lower knee touches floor, opposite elbow and shoulder blade touch floor	10
	Lower knee touches floor, opposite elbow and shoulder blade off floor	7
	Lower knee 1–3 inches off floor	5
	Lower knee more than 3 inches off floor	1

To obtain your overall score, add the individual scores for the nine tests. Turn to p. 44 to rate your score.

3. MUSCLE STRENGTH AND ENDURANCE

We will use just two tests to get a rough idea of your current level of strength: total number of push-ups, and number of sit-ups performed in 60 seconds.

The push-ups are done with the knees off the ground if you are a man and with knees on the ground if you are a woman (see figs. 14 and 15).

The sit-ups are done with your knees bent and with your feet hooked under a chair or bed. In addition, your hands should be crossed in front of

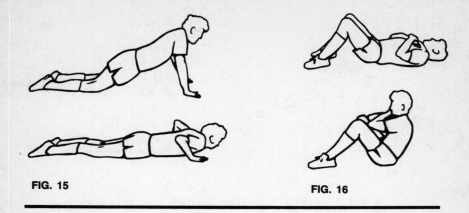

FIG. 15

FIG. 16

your chest during the sit-up exercise, as shown in fig. 16. Have a friend time you for exactly 60 seconds.

Push-ups

Strength and Endurance Category	Number completed
Excellent	40 or more
Good	24–39
Fair	16–23
Poor	15 or fewer

Sit-ups

Strength and Endurance Category	Number completed in 60 seconds
Excellent	40 or more
Good	30–39
Fair	20–29
Poor	19 or fewer

For your score on both exercises, see p. 44.

4. Body Fat/Ideal Weight

There are two methods to estimate your body fat. One method involves simple arithmetic to estimate your desirable weight, while the other is to have your body fat actually measured in a laboratory. The first method, outlined below, is simpler, but the other is more accurate.

Calculating Ideal Weight

For men:
    a. Record the number of inches in your height over 5' and multiply this number by 6.
    b. Add 106.
       (EXAMPLE: If you are male and 5'8" tall,
                  $8 \times 6 = 48 + 106 = 154$ lbs. is your ideal weight.)

Calculate your ideal weight:

_____ × 6 = _____ + 106 = _____ your ideal weight.

Now weigh yourself.

Your weight = _____

$$\frac{\text{Your weight}}{\text{Your ideal weight}} = \underline{\quad}$$

Your % over or under ideal weight = _____

For women:
    a. Record the number of inches in your height over 5' and multiply this number by 5.
    b. Add 100.
       (EXAMPLE: If you are female and 5'4" tall,
                  $4 \times 5 = 20 + 100 = 120$ lbs. is your ideal weight.)

Calculate your ideal weight:

_____ × 5 = _____ + 100 = _____ your ideal weight.

Now weigh yourself.

Your weight = _____

$$\frac{\text{Your weight}}{\text{Your ideal weight}} = \underline{\quad}$$

Your % over or under ideal weight = _____

See p. 45 to score your percentage over or under ideal weight.

5. MENTAL BALANCE

To assess your level of mental preparation for performance, circle the number which best describes your behavior in each of the following situations:

	Often	Sometimes	Rarely
1. Overreact when pressured	0	5	10
2. Criticize yourself severely when you make mistakes	0	5	10
3. Worry excessively about things beyond your control	0	5	10
4. Make excuses for yourself when you perform poorly	0	5	10
5. Procrastinate or avoid preparing adequately for tasks which have to be done and done well	0	5	10
6. Lose confidence in yourself	0	5	10
7. Get more tense when trying to relax	0	5	10
8. Do much of what you do mechanically and halfheartedly	0	5	10
9. Feel that the harder you work, the less you seem to get done	0	5	10
10. Have difficulty getting out of ruts and bad habits which reduce your effectiveness	0	5	10

To calculate your mental balance score, total the number of points. Turn to p. 45 to rate your score.

6. CARDIAC RISK FACTORS

The goal for cardiac risk factors is to keep your score as low as possible. Fill out the following questionnaire by placing an X in the appropriate blank, and then total up your points.

	Available Points		Your Score

1. Your age
		M	F	
20–29	____	2	2	
30–39	____	2	2	
40–49	____	6	2	
50–59	____	14	6	
60–69	____	18	14	
70–79	____	20	18	____

2. Cigarette smoking
   a. Currently smoke 1 or more packs of cigarettes a day ____   10
   b. Currently smoke less than 1 pack of cigarettes a day ____   7
   c. You were once a cigarette smoker but stopped less than a year ago ____   4
   d. You were once a cigarette smoker but stopped a year ago ____   3
   e. Never smoked ____   1   ____

3. Your current blood pressure (If not known, have it measured by a health care professional or friend.) ____
   a. Systolic blood pressure greater than or equal to 160 mmHg ____   5
   b. Systolic blood pressure greater than 140 mmHg but less than 160 mmHg ____   3
   c. Systolic blood pressure less than or equal to 140 mmHg ____   1
   d. Diastolic blood pressure greater than or equal to 100 mmHg ____   5
   e. Diastolic blood pressure greater than 90 mmHg but less than 100 mmHg ____   3
   f. Diastolic blood pressure less than or equal to 90 mmHg ____   1   ____

	Available Points	Your Score
4A. Blood cholesterol level, if known (Every adult should have a random blood cholesterol level done once every 5 years.)		
a. Cholesterol greater than or equal to 265 ____	10	
b. Cholesterol greater than 230 but less than 265 ____	7	
c. Cholesterol greater than 200 but less than or equal to 230 ____	5	
d. Cholesterol less than or equal to 200 ____	3	____
4B. If your blood cholesterol level is not known, answer the following:		
a. Red meat eaten more than 4 times per week ____	5	
b. Red meat eaten 4 times or less per week ____	3	
c. More than 2 eggs eaten per week ____	5	
d. Two eggs or fewer eaten per week ____	2	____
5. Family history: Has any sibling or either parent had any of the following before the age of 60?		
Coronary artery disease		
Heart attack		
Stroke		
Sudden death		
Angina Yes ____	10	
No ____	2	____
6. Do you have diabetes? Yes ____	10	
No ____	2	____
7. Classify your current weight. (If you are uncertain of your ideal weight, ask a health professional.)		
a. More than 50 pounds overweight ____	10	
b. 21 to 50 pounds overweight ____	8	
c. 10 to 20 pounds overweight ____	6	
d. More than ideal body weight but less than 10 pounds overweight ____	3	

	Available Points	Your Score
e. Ideal body weight or less ___	1	___
8. Characterize the amount of stress in your life.		
a. Constant, heavy stress ___	10	
b. Moderate stress ___	6	
c. Light or no stress ___	2	___
9. Characterize the amount of exercise you get.		
a. Light: You have a sit-down job and no regular organized physical activity. ___	10	
b. Moderate: Usual job activities might include climbing stairs or light lifting. You are sporadically involved in recreational athletics. ___	8	
c. Heavy: You participate in regular vigorous physical activity on a daily basis at work or participate in at least 45 minutes of vigorous leisure sports at least 4 times/week. ___	3	___
Your total points		___

See p. 46 for overall scoring of your cardiac risk factors.

7. POSITIVE LIFESTYLE

While many components contribute to a positive lifestyle, here we emphasize a few that we believe are particularly important. In the following questionnaire, points are rewarded for practices that contribute to a positive lifestyle. Place an X in the appropriate blank and record your points.

	Available Points	Your Score
1A. Do you have a personal physician?		
Yes ____	5	
No ____	0	____
1B. Have you had a checkup with a physician within the past 3 years?		
Yes ____	5	
No ____	0	____
2A. Do you have a personal dentist?		
Yes ____	5	
No ____	0	____
2B. Have you had a dental checkup within the last 6 months?		
Yes ____	5	
No ____	0	____
3. Do you regularly perform cancer self-screening, including either breast or testicular self-examination?		
Yes ____	10	
No ____	0	____
4. Have you established a deep, loving relationship with another individual?		
Yes ____	10	
No ____	0	____
5. Would you characterize the communication in your family as open and loving?		
Yes ____	10	
No ____	0	____
6. Characterize the amount of alcohol you consume.		
Low ____	10	
Moderate ____	5	
Heavy ____	0	____
7. Do you regularly use a seat belt when driving and insist that your passengers wear them as well?		
Yes ____	10	
No ____	0	____
8. Are you trained to perform cardiopulmonary resuscitation in an emergency?		
Yes ____	10	
No ____	0	____

	Available Points	Your Score
9. Have you and all the members of your family learned basic water safety techniques?		
Yes _____	10	
No _____	0	_____
10. Do you have a first aid kit in your home?		
Yes _____	5	
No _____	0	_____
11. Have you and all the members of your family learned basic first aid techniques?		
Yes _____	5	
No _____	0	_____
Your total points		_____

See p. 46 to rate your positive lifestyle score.

SCORING YOURSELF FOR SPORTS PERFORMANCE

In this section we will put all the Sports Performance tests together to develop a composite score. We will also direct you to the appropriate places in the book to begin an exercise program, or to work on areas in which you scored poorly.

The following points are available:

Aerobic Capacity	300
Flexibility	100
Muscular Strength and Endurance	100
Body Fat	100
Mental Balance	100
Cardiac Risk Factors	200
Positive Lifestyle	100
Total =	1000

1. Aerobic Capacity

Circle your aerobic fitness level below. Then record the number of points scored. The location of the aerobic action plan for you is indicated in the final column.

Aerobic Fitness Level (circle one)

	Aerobic fitness points	Location of your aerobic action plan
Poor	60	pp. 63, 70, 77, 85, 91
Fair	120	pp. 64, 71, 78, 86, 92
Average	180	pp. 65, 72, 79, 87, 93
Good	240	pp. 66, 73, 80, 88, 94
Excellent	300	pp. 67, 74, 81, 89, 95

Your total Aerobic Fitness points = ____

2. Flexibility

Record your flexibility score here: ____
    A score of 80–100 reflects a high level of flexibility.
    A score of 50–79 reflects moderate flexibility.
    A score below 50 reflects low flexibility.
    If you have a total score in the moderate or low category, you can probably benefit from regular stretching work as described in chapter 3. Remember that regular work at your limits leads naturally to increased flexibility.

3. Muscle Strength and Endurance

a. Upper body strength and endurance
Record your category from the push-up test here: _____
The following points are available:
       Excellent   50
       Good   40
       Fair   20
       Poor   10
Record your number of points here: ____

b. Abdominal strength and endurance
    Record your category from the 60-second sit-up test here: _____
    The following points are available:
       Excellent   50
       Good   40
       Fair   20
       Poor   10
Record your number of points here: ____

Total number of strength and endurance points scored (a + b): ____

Total score	Strength and endurance category
90–100	Excellent
70–89	Good
40–69	Fair
Below 40	Poor

4. Body Fat

If you chose the calculation method, record your percentage over ideal weight here (if you are at ideal weight record 0): ____%

SCORING

Weight	Category	Points
at ideal body weight	trim	100
1–10% over ideal weight	average	80
11–20% over ideal weight	above average	60
21–30% over ideal weight	fat	40
over 30% over ideal weight	over fat	20

If you had your body fat measured in a laboratory or at a physician's office, record the percentage of body fat here: ____%

SCORING

% body fat (men)	% body fat (women)	Category	Points
7–12	14–19	trim	100
13–16	20–23	average	80
17–19	24–26	above average	60
20–25	27–30	fat	40
over 25	over 30	over fat	20

5. Mental Balance

Record your score for mental balance here: ____

A score of 70–100 is excellent. Whatever you are doing, just keep it up.

A score of 40–69 is average.

A score below 40 is below average. If you score below 40 on this test, you may want to consider taking the suggestions in chapter 5 very seriously and begin to work systematically to deepen your ability to relax and concentrate.

6. Cardiac Risk Factors

Record the points you scored for cardiac risk factors here: _____

The scoring for cardiac risk factors is as follows (total available points = 100):

Less than 25	Very low risk
25–29	Low risk
30–39	Moderate risk
40–49	Moderately high risk
50 or above	High risk

If you are in the
  Very low risk category: Congratulations! Continue your healthy lifestyle.
  Low risk category: This is very good, but even further reduction of your risk
    may be achieved through careful assessment of your lifestyle and habits.
  Moderate risk category: This is average. You should give careful considera-
    tion to your lifestyle and habits to try to lower your risk of coronary heart
    disease.
  Moderately high risk category: This is too high. It is important that you modify
    your lifestyle and habits to reduce your risk of coronary heart disease.
  High risk category: This is much too high. It is extremely important that you
    modify your lifestyle and habits to reduce your risk of coronary heart dis-
    ease. You should discuss this with a health care professional.

We are now going to convert the risk factor categories into Sports Performance points. In this transformation, the *lower* your risk factors, the *more* Sports
Performance points you score.

Risk Category	Sports Performance Points
Very low	200
Low	160
Moderate	120
Moderately high	80
High	40

Your Sports Performance points for cardiac risk factors: _____

7. Positive Lifestyle

Record the points that you scored for positive lifestyle: _____

The scoring for positive lifestyle is as follows:

80–100 points	Excellent
60–79 points	Average
Below 60 points	Below average

If you score above 80 points you have already made a major commitment to
positive lifestyle. Keep up the good work.

If you score between 60 and 80 points, you are taking average care of your
lifestyle. Improvements can come from attention to some of the issues raised in
chapter 13.

If you score below 60 points, you should attempt to follow the guidelines in
chapter 13 to adopt more positive lifestyle habits.

OVERALL SCORING FOR SPORTS PERFORMANCE

Here we summarize your overall Sports Performance score. Record each of your scores in the spaces provided, then total up your score.

CATEGORY	TOTAL AVAILABLE POINTS	YOUR SCORE
1. Aerobic Capacity	300	_____
2. Flexibility	100	_____
3. Muscle Strength and Endurance	100	_____
4. Body Fat	100	_____
5. Mental Balance	100	_____
6. Cardiac Risk Factors	200	_____
7. Positive Lifestyle	100	_____
Total = 1000		Your Total = _____

A total Sports Performance score above 900 is excellent and indicates you already have a great commitment to health and fitness.

A score of 700–900 is average. There is plenty of room to improve in individual areas.

If your score is below 700 you should actively seek ways of improving your score in each of the 7 Building Blocks.

We recommend that you retest yourself every three months to monitor your progress on the Sports Performance tests.

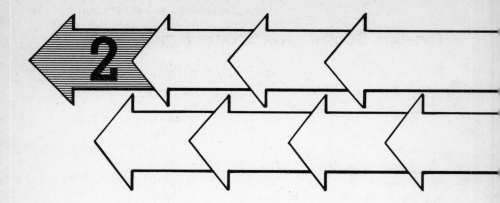

Aerobic conditioning is a vital element of any total fitness program. A number of different terms have been employed to describe aerobic conditioning, including aerobic capacity, cardiovascular endurance and aerobic power. Excellent aerobic conditioning is essential to such endurance athletes as marathon runners or long-distance swimmers. More and more, however, athletes from other sports have come to understand the value of good aerobic conditioning.

We've noticed increased interest in aerobic conditioning over the past three years in spring-training testing with the Boston Red Sox. Each year the players report to camp in better aerobic condition. They recognize that this conditioning will enhance performance and decrease the chance of injury. Even some athletes in such sports as golf which have been thought to have little aerobic component have adopted endurance exercise programs. They recognize that fatigue can result in lapses in mental concentration. The sporting community is filled with teams and individuals who have improved their performance because of increased attention to aerobic conditioning—examples range all the way from the tennis player Martina Navratilova to football teams that wear their opponents down in the third and fourth quarters.

The lessons these athletes have learned about the importance of aerobic conditioning can also be important to you in your daily life.

AEROBIC AND ANAEROBIC CAPACITY

The major source of energy production and the most efficient system the body has for endurance exercise is from the aerobic system. Aerobic means "in the presence of air." What this signifies is that when you begin to exercise, the muscles call for increased energy in order to work. To

Aerobic

Conditioning

supply this energy, both a source of fuel to be burned (in this case glucose) and oxygen to support the combustion are required. Both of these are carried via the bloodstream. To support high levels of exercise, the heart, lungs and muscles must all work harder.

The aerobic system is well suited to meet the needs of long-term endurance exercise. To meet the needs of short-term exercise, to provide short-term support until the aerobic system can take over, and to provide a "fail-safe" system during periods of extreme exertion, the body also has the anaerobic system. Anaerobic means "occurring in the absence of air." This system allows the body to get extra energy in the absence of oxygen. For example, when you begin to exercise, energy consumption starts long before the effects of increased heart and lung function can be felt. Anaerobic metabolism supports this early energy use. It also supports short bursts of activity. The 100-yard dash, shot put, fast break in a basketball game, or 40-yard touchdown run are supported virtually 100 percent by anaerobic metabolism.

The final situation in which anaerobic metabolism assumes great importance is during periods of extreme exertion. The marathon runner or long-distance cyclist or swimmer who has to sprint the last minute of a race will frequently exceed his or her aerobic capacity. In this setting the athlete can employ anaerobic metabolism for brief periods to produce the extra energy needed.

While the anaerobic system thus provides a useful adjunct to the aerobic system, it is much less efficient. Anaerobic metabolism can be viewed as a short-term loan which must be paid back rapidly and with a high interest rate. When energy is produced through the anaerobic system, the waste product lactic acid is also produced, causing muscle burning and fatigue. Thus, high levels of anaerobic energy production can be sustained only for very short periods of time—usually less than two minutes, even in well-conditioned and highly motivated individuals.

AN ANAEROBIC THRESHOLD

The concept of "anaerobic threshold" is a relatively new one. However, it has assumed increasing importance in the training of professional and Olympic athletes. It is the point at which a significant amount of energy is produced without oxygen.

Most exercise physiologists would agree that the maximum total body oxygen consumption ($maxVO_2$) provides the best single estimate of a person's overall aerobic capacity. As a performance criterion, however, it leaves a lot to be desired. If you took two individuals with identical maximum total body oxygen consumption and on the basis of this number tried to predict how fast they would run a 10-kilometer race or a marathon, the chances are that you would make significant errors.

In an experiment in our laboratory, we followed two relatively fit individuals who were each training for their first marathon. One was a 37-year-old man (Runner A) who had averaged 30 miles a week for the five years prior to the marathon and the other was a 28-year-old man (Runner B) who had averaged 35–40 miles a week for approximately the same number of years. For the three months prior to the race we measured their maximum total body oxygen consumption every two weeks. Both runners improved significantly over the twelve-week period. By the end of the training period, both had reached a very high level of maximum total body oxygen consumption. However, when they ran the marathon, Runner B was able to run it in 2 hours and 42 minutes while Runner A ran it in 3 hours and 54 minutes. The difference was that Runner B had a much higher anaerobic threshold than Runner A. Runner A had an anaerobic threshold of 63% of his maximum total body oxygen consumption while Runner B had an anaerobic threshold of 83% of his maximum total body oxygen consumption. When we took these differences in the anaerobic threshold into account, we were able to predict each runner's eventual time to within several minutes over the 26-mile race!

There is little argument that with training, an individual can improve his or her anaerobic threshold. Thus, an average individual achieves an anaerobic threshold at 50–60% of maximum total body oxygen consumption while a world-class marathoner, cyclist or rower may not hit anaerobic threshold until 80–90% of maximum total body oxygen consumption. For such an individual, the increase in even 1–2% in anaerobic threshold could mean the difference between an excellent performance and a world record. Increasingly, training programs are being devised to try to squeeze out this extra 1–2%. This is one of the hottest areas of athletic performance research and you are going to hear a lot more about it in the next few years.

THE BODY'S RESPONSE TO EXERCISE

In practice, the division between aerobic and anaerobic energy production is not clear-cut. As shown in fig. 17, the response to exercise involves changes in both aerobic and anaerobic systems.

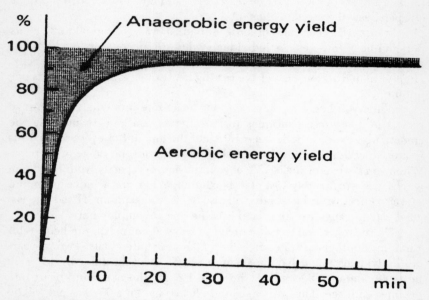

FIG. 17. From Åstrand and Rodahl, *Textbook of Work Physiology*, with permission.

The initial energy production comes almost exclusively from the anaerobic system. However, by one minute into exercise, about half of the energy production is coming from the aerobic system and about half from the anaerobic system. Within three minutes from the start of exercise, 90% of the energy production results from the aerobic system.

When you begin to exercise, an increasing amount of energy is burned. In order to support this higher level of combustion, both increased glucose and oxygen must be burned. The best way we have of measuring how much work is being performed is to measure the amount of oxygen being consumed. We call this figure the total body oxygen consumption. The total body oxygen consumption (abbreviated VO_2) is a combination of how well the heart supplies oxygenated blood to the exercising muscles and how efficiently these muscles are able to get the oxygen from the blood. When you train, both of these processes improve.

THE CARDIAC RESPONSE TO EXERCISE

For every bodily function—from digesting food to muscle contraction during exercise—to occur, a source of oxygenated blood to support energy combustion is needed. The heart supplies this oxygenated blood.

The amount of blood the heart pumps out per minute is known as the *cardiac output*. Two components make up the cardiac output, how fast the heart beats per minute (the *heart rate*) and how much blood it pumps out per beat (the *stroke volume*).

At rest, the heart rate in most individuals varies from 60 to 80 beats per minute. However, in individuals who are anxious or in very poor condition, a resting heart rate of over 100 beats per minute may occur. Highly trained athletes may have resting heart rates as low as 40 beats per minute.

When you begin to exercise, your heart rate immediately begins to rise. The heart rate continues to rise as you continue to increase the amount you exercise. The heart rate and the amount of exercise are thus related to each other in a direct fashion throughout the range of exercise. When you are exercising at 75% of your maximum capacity, your heart rate will be at approximately 75% of its maximum. When you achieve maximum exercise effort, your heart rate will also be at its maximum. Heart rate is a good way to gauge exertion, and it is the one we employ here.

There are several facts you need to know about maximum heart rate. First, maximum heart rates are different among individuals. Two 25-year-old individuals might have maximum heart rates that differ by 15 or 20 beats per minute. Second, as shown in fig. 18, the maximum heart rate declines with age. Thus, the maximum heart rate for a 65-year-old will be significantly slower than for a 25-year-old. You can determine your maximum heart rate from the figure or use the rule of thumb that your maximum heart rate is equal to 220 minus your age in years.

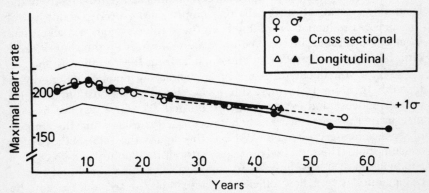

FIG. 18. From Åstrand and Rodahl, *Textbook of Work Physiology*, with permission.

In contrast to the heart rate, the stroke volume increases when you begin to exercise, then levels off. By the time you are at approximately 50% of your maximum exertion, your stroke volume is at 100% of its maximum. The extra blood flow required to support exertion of 50–100% of maximum comes almost exclusively from increases in heart rate.

When you are sitting still, your heart pumps about 5 liters of blood per minute. When you exert yourself to a maximum extent, the output can increase to 25 to 30 liters per minute. A large, well-trained athlete may achieve a cardiac output of up to 40 liters per minute! The heart is truly a magnificent pump.

ADAPTATIONS OF THE HEART AND MUSCLES TO ENDURANCE EXERCISE

Many scientific studies have shown that exercise causes significant improvements in aerobic capacity. These changes are called "the training effect." Some of the changes include a decrease in resting heart rate, increase in maximum total body oxygen consumption, decrease in percentage of maximum total body oxygen consumption at levels less than maximum exertion, and increase in the anaerobic threshold.

Decrease in resting heart rate. When you engage in consistent endurance training, you call upon your heart to pump large volumes of blood regularly. One way which the heart adapts to this "overload" situation over time is that it grows slightly larger. This allows more blood to be pumped out per beat (larger stroke volume). It used to be thought that the somewhat larger hearts commonly observed in athletes might represent some bad consequence of exercise, and it was even labeled the "athlete's heart syndrome." Now we know that these enlargements represent a normal response to endurance exercise and that they indicate a healthy adaptation.

The reason that your resting heart rate decreases as your aerobic capacity improves is very simple. At rest, your body's energy needs are no different from what they were before you started a training program. So the amount of blood required at rest does not change from before a conditioning program to after. However, after an endurance training program the amount of blood pumped out per beat increases and the same amount of blood can be pumped with fewer beats per minute.

Increase in maximum total body oxygen consumption. The maximum total body oxygen consumption is regarded by most exercise physiologists as the "gold standard" for measuring an individual's overall aerobic capacity. As we have already indicated, the total body oxygen consumption represents the combination of the blood pumped and the ability of the muscles to extract oxygen from the blood.

Numerous studies have shown that the maximum total body oxygen consumption (and hence the aerobic capacity) improves with endurance training programs. Improvements of 15–20% over a six-month training period may occur, and changes as high as 40–50% are possible for some individuals, particularly if they have been very sedentary.

Decrease in the percentage of maximum total body oxygen consumption at levels of exertion that are less than maximum. The fact that after endurance training, tasks can be performed using a smaller percentage of maximum capacity carries important implications for day-to-day living and recreational sports. It means you will have more energy at the end of a working day. It means that you will experience less fatigue after playing several sets of tennis. (And maybe even win that third set when your opponent tires!)

The increased energy individuals experience following endurance training is so common that individuals who have excellent aerobic capacity wouldn't think of stopping exercise. They know that their daily exercise routines are key to maintaining highly productive lifestyles. Far from taking time out to exercise, these individuals make a daily investment in exercise, realizing that both the short-term benefits of increased energy and productivity and the long-term health benefits are impressive.

Increased anaerobic threshold. Preliminary studies in our laboratory and in others suggest that increases in anaerobic threshold continue to occur even after changes in the maximum total body oxygen consumption have reached a plateau. This is an area of tremendous research interest with considerable practical application. For Olympic athletes, we foresee training programs based on anaerobic threshold which will continue to push back the boundaries of human performance. For recreational athletes, training programs based on an understanding of individuals' anaerobic thresholds will help them achieve their very best.

TRAINING TO IMPROVE AEROBIC CAPACITY

All of the aerobic conditioning programs outlined in this book are based on sound scientific principles and are designed to offer solid general guidelines to improve your aerobic capacity. While these programs offer general guidance, an individualized training program will ultimately be based on a person's specific goals and aspirations. The programs we out-line will provide an excellent format for the individual seeking to improve overall aerobic fitness. But they would hardly be adequate for the world-class or Olympic athlete. That's because for such an athlete the *goals* of training are quite different from those for the average individual. We have recommended that you perform aerobic workouts three times a week, yet the average Olympic athlete will work out six or seven days a week. The key point is to formulate your goals clearly, then individualize your training program to achieve them.

Three general principles guide any program of endurance training. Several investigators have put these together to form the word FIT. The principles are these:

Frequency
Intensity
Time

By *frequency* we mean how many times a week you participate in endurance training. We have suggested three times a week for several reasons. First, many studies have shown that this frequency of training is sufficient for most individuals to achieve significant improvements in aerobic capacity. Second, this gives you enough free time in the week to alternate your endurance workouts with musculoskeletal strength build-ing, a combination we believe is important for total fitness. It also still leaves time for one or two days away from training each week, another concept we believe is essential to allow the body to recover and rebuild.

By *intensity* we mean how hard you are working during the aerobic workout. Monitoring your heart rate during exercise is the most practical way of assessing the intensity of the work. Our guidelines, which take you from 60% to 80% of your maximum predicted heart rate, provide an excellent range for improving aerobic capacity in the average individual. For the high-level competitive athlete, these guidelines will not produce sufficient stress to improve performance significantly. Such athletes will regularly induce periods of exertion to 100% of predicted maximum heart rate to achieve their performance goals. Such periods of "all-out" stress are not necessary and may even be dangerous for the recreational athlete. At the very least they are psychologically draining. Remember, the goals of the top competitive athlete are probably quite different from yours.

By *time* we mean the amount of time needed in an aerobic workout to achieve maximum benefit for your heart. You will notice that all of our aerobic workouts vary from 20 to 60 minutes, time frames which are sufficient to achieve excellent aerobic fitness benefits. Once again, top competitive endurance athletes may spend considerably more time each day in training.

SOME SPECIAL CONSIDERATIONS IN AEROBIC CAPACITY

Genetic Background

One famous exercise physiologist is said to have commented, "The Olympic endurance athlete would do well to select his parents carefully." This tongue-in-cheek remark points up a fundamental truth which has become increasingly important at the highest levels of athletic performance. That is the fact that genetic endowment can play a significant role in an athlete's ability to perform, particularly in endurance sports. Some exercise scientists have estimated that 70% of your aerobic capacity is determined by genetic factors while the remaining 30% is subject to change by training. This fact has been central to the recent Olympic success of athletes from some Eastern bloc nations, where concerted efforts are made to test young athletes and identify those with exceptional capacity for intensive training. While it is true that such genetic capacity won't tell you which athletes will have the competitive fire and will to win that will make them champions, it is also true that an individual with a below-average total body oxygen consumption is never going to win an Olympic marathon.

Interval Training versus Long, Slow Distance Training

There are two basic approaches to training to improve aerobic capacity: interval training and long, slow distance training. Both have their advantages and disadvantages. For top competitive athletes, training programs are typically a combination of the two approaches. We have chosen the long, slow distance approach as the basis of the aerobic exercise prescriptions in this book for several reasons. First, we believe that it is the safest approach for the average individual seeking improved fitness. Second, it has been proven effective for achieving aerobic fitness goals. Third, it is much less psychologically draining than the interval training approach.

Interval training involves periods of intense exercise done within set time intervals followed by set time intervals of lighter exercise or rest. An example of an interval training set for a competitive swimmer might be as follows:

Set 1: 8 × 100 yards freestyle at 60 seconds. Each 100-yard interval is followed by 30 seconds rest.

Set 2: 8 × 200 yards freestyle at 2 minutes. Each 200-yard interval is followed by 60 seconds rest.

Virtually every college swimming team and track team now base at least some portion of their workouts on the interval concept. The concept of interval training has been given major credit for the dramatic decline in swimming and track record times over the past twenty years. We would, however, encourage you to stick with the long, slow distance conditioning programs we have outlined in this book.

Training for Improved Aerobic Capacity and Weight Loss

Regular aerobic exercise is a key component to long-term, effective weight loss. Many scientists used to believe that the major fuel burned during exercise was glycogen. Now we realize that fat is an important fuel during exercise. This is particularly true of long bouts of exercise at submaximal levels. Work is currently in progress to determine exactly the best levels and durations of aerobic exercise to help people lose fat.

Aerobic Capacity and Aging

Many studies have shown that aerobic capacity declines with age. However, it has also been shown that the *rate* of decline can be significantly slowed by regular endurance exercise programs. Recently we studied twelve individuals who were enrolled in a regular walking program. Over a three-month period the average increase in aerobic capacity was 12%. How old were these people? The *youngest* was 70 years old and the average age was 74! We believe the medical profession has vastly underestimated the vigor of our healthy elderly population. We regularly prescribe aerobic exercise to healthy individuals regardless of their age.

Aerobic Capacity in Cardiac Rehabilitation

Tremendous strides in improving aerobic capacity can be achieved in individuals who have suffered heart attacks or are recovering from open heart surgery. These improvements in aerobic capacity are typically accompanied by improved energy and lifestyle. Indeed, many of these individuals receive a new lease on life through improved aerobic capacity and risk factor reduction.

AEROBIC CONDITIONING
ACTION PLANS

Next we will help you plan an aerobic fitness program. Even if you're very eager to begin a personal fitness program, it is very important that you read the previous chapter, and do the self-tests. This will tell you your level of fitness and give you the specific information you need to choose the action plan designed for your level of fitness. Pretesting will also make the action plans safer and more enjoyable for you.

No one should start a new exercise program without clearance from his or her doctor. If you have any questions about the safety of an exercise program for you, see your doctor.

You will find action plans for improving your aerobic capacity. Since we believe that flexibility is important, we have also included specific stretching routines at the beginning of each set of action plans for aerobic conditioning.

To determine your appropriate aerobic conditioning program, two pieces of information are needed:

1. Your current aerobic fitness level
2. Your choice of aerobic sport

Your current aerobic fitness level should be determined by one of the four self-tests outlined in chapter 1. The following equivalences have been established between fitness level and aerobic action plan:

Fitness level (determined by self-test)	Aerobic action plan
poor	starter
fair	beginner
average	intermediate
good	advanced
excellent	expert

Your choice of aerobic sport will depend largely on personal preference, climate and availability of facilities. We have given you 20-week aerobic conditioning action plans for the following five aerobic sports:

The action plans have been carefully formulated to give an appropriate cardiovascular workout for your current level of conditioning. Each is slowly progressive over 20 weeks. We recommend that you retest yourself after completion of a program to determine your next program level.

Learning Your Target Heart Rate

All individuals serious about improving aerobic capacity should learn how to determine their target heart rate to ensure that maximum aerobic benefits are achieved during periods of aerobic exercise. All of the aerobic conditioning programs are based on target heart rates, so you must learn how to take your pulse and calculate your heart rate. The techniques are really very simple, but they require a little patience, practice and some simple arithmetic.

Step 1: Feel the pulse of the artery at your wrist (the radial pulse). Feel the pulse at one wrist with the fingertips of the other hand. Time the pulse with the second hand of a watch or clock. Count the number of beats for 15 seconds then multiply by four to determine the number of heartbeats per minute. For example, if while relaxing you count 18 beats in 15 seconds, your resting heart rate is 18 × 4, or 72, beats per minute.

Step 2: Compute your maximum predicted heart rate. The easiest way is to take 220 beats per minute and subtract your age. For example, if you are 45 years old, your predicted maximum heart rate is 220 minus 45, or 175, beats per minute.

Step 3: Determine your target heart rate zone. Multiply your maximum heart rate by 70% and by 80%. For our 45-year-old, the target zone lies between 175 × 70% (175 × .7) and 175 × 80% (175 × .8), or between 123 and 140 beats per minute.

Step 4: Now, after stretching, begin to exercise, following the instructions outlined for week 1 in the category in which your fitness self-test placed you. Spend the first few minutes slowly building up your amount of exercise. When you have reached a comfortable pace, determine your pulse rate as described above. If you are below your target zone, speed up. If you are above the target zone, slow down. Once you are in the target zone, maintain this pace for the recommended time, checking your pulse rate every five minutes. After you have followed this routine a few times you will be able to estimate your heart rate with fewer actual measurements.

The aerobic action plans were developed in our laboratories. Don't be intimidated by them. They are designed to build up your aerobic capacity gradually and make your heart stronger.

STARTER PROGRAMS

If you scored in the "poor" category of the aerobic capacity tests, then the Starter Programs are for you. You have a ways to go, but you stand to benefit the most from aerobic exercise. Just pick your aerobic exercise and turn to the Starter Program.

The hardest part will be the first several weeks. You may have not had regular exercise for years, so give yourself a chance to ease into the program. Make a commitment to yourself to stick with it. Plan a specific time each day for your exercise. Find a friend to exercise with you.

Record your workout and how you feel each day in a logbook. This is very important and will give you a sense of what you have accomplished. An appointment book or calendar can make an excellent exercise logbook.

Remember not to take any shortcuts. Learn how to take your pulse. Make sure you do the stretches outlined for each sport both before and after exercising.

BEGINNER PROGRAMS

If you scored in the "fair" category on the aerobic capacity tests, then the Beginner Programs are for you. Chances are that if you're in this category, you do have some light exercise in your daily routine but don't set aside a specific period for regular, vigorous exercise.

Regular exercise will help you organize your time, and you'll be amazed at the extra energy it gives you. Don't be surprised if it takes a while to get used to the regular period of exercise. It took you a while to get out of shape, so be patient with yourself as you get back into shape.

Develop a plan to help you approach aerobic exercise. Be sure to do the stretches outlined for each sport both before and after each exercise session. Record your daily progress in your logbook. By the end of the 20 weeks you'll be ready to move into one of the more advanced protocols.

INTERMEDIATE PROGRAMS

If you scored in the "average" category on the aerobic capacity tests, then the Intermediate Programs are for you. It is possible that you are already involved in some recreational activities or have completed either the Starter or the Beginner Programs.

The Intermediate Programs are designed to help you take the next step to a lifelong commitment to regular, vigorous exercise. Don't be surprised if you find your aerobic exercise program more strenuous than you anticipated. Most of the Intermediate exercise protocols are at least as strenuous as vigorous singles tennis.

This is the time to make a true commitment to physical conditioning and strengthening your heart. Your Intermediate Program will get you started on a lifetime of health exercise.

ADVANCED PROGRAMS

If you scored in the "good" category on the aerobic capacity tests, then the Advanced Programs are for you. If you are in this category, you have already made a commitment to regular exercise.

In the Advanced Programs you begin with vigorous aerobic exercises and focus on building an even higher aerobic capacity than you currently enjoy.

EXPERT PROGRAMS

If you scored in the "excellent" category on the aerobic capacity tests, then the Expert Programs are for you. Congratulations! You have already made a serious commitment to regular exercise. You rate in the top 5% of individuals in the United States.

The main purpose of the Expert Programs is to help you formalize an already high level of activity and commitment. These programs also allow you to draw equivalents between sports to insure that your workouts are consistent from season to season.

Maintenance Programs

When you arrive at this section it means you have conscientiously applied yourself to at least 20 weeks of aerobic exercise. Or you are at an advanced or expert level and want a maintenance program of aerobic exercise to add structure to your workouts. In either case, you have made a lifelong commitment to improved health through aerobic exercise.

FITNESS WALKING

Walking is a wonderful and vastly underrated form of aerobic exercise. Fitness walking, by which we mean walking at a determined pace to get your heart rate up into the target training zone, is one of the best ways we know to build a lifelong program of aerobic conditioning.

We have a particularly strong commitment to walking. A number of research projects are under way in our laboratories, and one of us coauthored the previously mentioned book on the subject, *Fitness Walking*. Virtually every cardiac rehabilitation patient we see is started on a fitness walking program.

One of the reasons we are so enthusiastic about walking is that it's so simple. All you need is a good pair of shoes designed for serious walking and you can start this excellent form of aerobic exercise.

Stretching Routine for Fitness Walking

Walking for fitness requires and deserves a good deal of stretching to maintain flexibility, especially in the legs and back. Practice this gentle sequence (see fig. 19) on a regular basis and see if it doesn't affect your standing posture and your carriage and gait as you walk.

Complete the entire sequence, holding each stretch for at least the number of breaths indicated and alternating sides when required. Remember to breathe slowly and deeply, from your belly. Consult chapter 3 for more information on the principles to keep in mind as you do this sequence. This 19-step routine should take you at least 12 minutes. Optimally, this stretching routine should be performed *before* fitness walking, and selected stretches should be done *after* fitness walking.

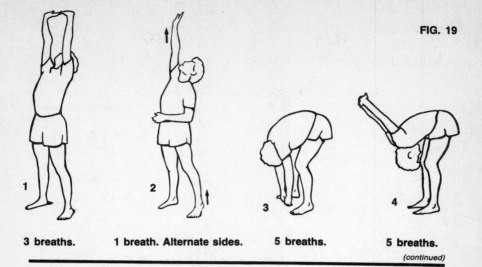

FIG. 19

1	2	3	4
3 breaths.	1 breath. Alternate sides.	5 breaths.	5 breaths.

(continued)

Fitness Walking: Starter Program

Week	Exercise	Mileage	Pace* (mph)	Heart rate (% of max.)	Duration of workout (min.)	Calories burned†	Frequency (times/wk.)
1	Fitness walk	1.00	3.0	60	20	100	3
2	Fitness walk	1.00	3.0	60	20	100	3
3	Fitness walk	1.25	3.0	60	25	125	3
4	Fitness walk	1.25	3.0	60	25	125	3
5	Fitness walk	1.50	3.0	60	30	150	3
6	Fitness walk	1.50	3.5	65–70	26	150	3
7	Fitness walk	1.75	3.5	65–70	30	175	3
8	Fitness walk	1.75	3.5	65–70	30	175	3
9	Fitness walk	2.00	3.5	65–70	34	200	3
10	Fitness walk	2.00	3.75	65–70	32	200	3
11	Fitness walk	2.00	3.75	70–75	32	200	3
12	Fitness walk	2.25	3.75	70–75	36	225	3
13	Fitness walk	2.25	3.75	70–75	36	225	3
14	Fitness walk	2.50	3.75	70–75	40	250	3
15	Fitness walk	2.50	4.0	70–75	38	250	3
16	Fitness walk	2.50	4.0	70–75	38	250	3
17	Fitness walk	2.75	4.0	75–80	41	275	3
18	Fitness walk	2.75	4.0	75–80	41	275	3
19	Fitness walk	2.75	4.0	75–80	45	275	3
20	Fitness walk	2.75	4.0	75–80	45	275	3

*The pace listed is only an approximation. The actual pace to be used is the one that keeps the heart rate at the appropriate % of max. listed.

†Calorie expenditure is for an average 150-pound person. The number of calories burned will be slightly lower for lower body weight and slightly higher for higher body weight.

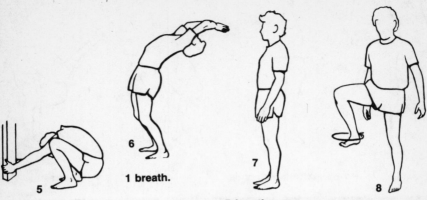

5 breaths.

6 1 breath.

7 5 breaths.

8 Crank foot 10 times each direction. Alternate sides.

Fitness Walking: Beginner Program

Week	Exercise	Mileage	Pace* (mph)	Heart rate (% of max.)	Duration of workout (min.)	Calories burned†	Frequency (times/wk.)
1	Fitness walk	1.50	3.0	60–65	30	150	3
2	Fitness walk	1.50	3.0	60–65	30	150	3
3	Fitness walk	1.75	3.0	60–65	35	175	3
4	Fitness walk	1.75	3.0	60–65	35	175	3
5	Fitness walk	2.00	3.0	60–65	40	200	3
6	Fitness walk	2.00	3.0	60–65	40	200	3
7	Fitness walk	2.00	3.5	65–70	34	200	3
8	Fitness walk	2.25	3.5	65–70	38	225	3
9	Fitness walk	2.25	3.5	65–70	38	225	3
10	Fitness walk	2.50	3.5	65–70	43	250	3
11	Fitness walk	2.50	3.5	65–70	43	250	3
12	Fitness walk	2.50	3.5	65–70	43	250	3
13	Fitness walk	2.75	3.5	65–70	47	275	3
14	Fitness walk	2.75	3.5	65–70	47	275	3
15	Fitness walk	3.00	4.0	70–80	45	300	3
16	Fitness walk	3.00	4.0	70–80	45	300	3
17	Fitness walk	3.00	4.0	70–80	45	300	3
18	Fitness walk	3.00	4.0	70–80	45	300	3
19	Fitness walk	3.00	4.0	70–80	45	300	3
20	Fitness walk	3.00	4.0	70–80	45	300	3

*The pace listed is only an approximation. The actual pace to be used is the one that keeps the heart rate at the appropriate % of max. listed.
†Calorie expenditure is for an average 150-pound person. The number of calories burned will be slightly lower for lower body weight and slightly higher for higher body weight.

11

10 breaths. Roll side to side.

10

9

10 breaths. Alternate sides.

12

10 breaths.

2 breaths, bouncing.

(continued)

Fitness Walking: Intermediate Program

Week	Exercise	Mileage	Pace* (mph)	Heart rate (% of max.)	Duration of workout (min.)	Calories burned†	Frequency (times/wk.)
1	Fitness walk	2.00	3.0	65–70	40	200	3
2	Fitness walk	2.25	3.0	65–70	45	225	3
3	Fitness walk	2.50	3.0	65–70	50	250	3
4	Fitness walk	2.50	3.0	65–70	50	250	3
5	Fitness walk	2.75	3.0	65–70	50	275	3
6	Fitness walk	2.75	3.5	70–75	47	275	3
7	Fitness walk	2.75	3.5	70–75	47	275	3
8	Fitness walk	2.75	3.5	70–75	47	275	3
9	Fitness walk	3.00	3.5	70–75	51	300	3
10	Fitness walk	3.00	3.5	70–75	51	300	3
11	Fitness walk	3.00	4.0	75–80	45	300	3
12	Fitness walk	3.00	4.0	75–80	45	300	3
13	Fitness walk	3.25	4.0	75–80	49	325	3
14	Fitness walk	3.25	4.0	75–80	49	325	3
15	Fitness walk	3.50	4.0	75–80	53	350	3
16	Fitness walk	3.50	4.5	75–80	47	350	3
17	Fitness walk	3.50	4.5	75–80	47	350	3
18	Fitness walk	3.50	4.5	75–80	47	350	3
19	Fitness walk	3.50	4.5	75–80	47	350	3
20	Fitness walk	3.50	4.5	75–80	47	350	3

*The pace listed is only an approximation. The actual pace to be used is the one that keeps the heart rate at the appropriate % of max. listed.

†Calorie expenditure is for an average 150-pound person. The number of calories burned will be slightly lower for lower body weight and slightly higher for higher body weight.

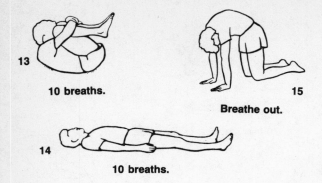

13 10 breaths.

14 10 breaths.

15 Breathe out.

16 Breathe in.
Alternate 5 times
between #15 and #16.

Fitness Walking: Advanced Program

Week	Exercise	Mileage	Pace* (mph)	Weight/ Incline**	Heart rate (% of max.)	Duration of workout (min.)	Calories burned†	Fre-quency (times /wk.)
1	Fitness walk	2.50	3.5		70–75	43	250	3
2	Fitness walk	2.75	3.5		70–75	47	275	3
3	Fitness walk	3.00	3.5		70–75	51	300	3
4	Fitness walk	3.00	3.5		70–75	51	300	3
5	Fitness walk	3.25	3.5		70–75	55	325	3
6	Fitness walk	3.25	4.0		75–80	49	325	3
7	Fitness walk	3.50	4.0		75–80	53	350	3
8	Fitness walk	3.75	4.5		75–80	50	375	3
9	Fitness walk	4.00	4.5		75–80	53	400	3
10	Fitness walk	4.00	4.5		75–80	53	400	3
11	Fitness walk	4.00	4.5		75–80	53	400	3
12	Fitness walk	4.00	4.5		75–80	53	400	3
13	Fitness walk	4.00	4.5		75–80	53	400	3
14	Fitness walk	4.00	4.5	+	75–80	53	>400‡	3
15	Fitness walk	4.00	4.5	+	75–80	53	>400‡	3
16	Fitness walk	4.00	4.5	+	75–80	53	>400‡	3
17	Fitness walk	4.00	4.5	+	75–80	53	>400‡	3
18	Fitness walk	4.00	4.5	+	75–80	53	>400‡	3
19	Fitness walk	4.00	4.5	+	75–80	53	>400‡	3
20	Fitness walk	4.00	4.5	+	75–80	53	>400‡	3

*The pace listed is only an approximation. The actual pace to be used is the one that keeps the heart rate at the appropriate % of max. listed.
**Weights (to upper body) or incline (hill walking) should be added as needed to keep heart rate in target zone (70–80% predicted maximum).
†Calorie expenditure is for an average 150-pound person. The number of calories burned will be slightly lower for lower body weight and slightly higher for higher body weight.
‡The exact number of calories burned will depend upon the amount of weight added.

17

Hold for 3 breaths.
Alternate sides. Do #15 in between.

18

10 breaths. Alternate sides.

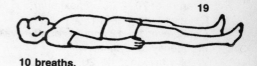

19

10 breaths.

Fitness Walking: Expert Program

Week	Exercise	Mileage	Pace* (mph)	Weight/ Incline**	Heart rate (% of max.)	Duration of workout (min.)	Calories burned†	Fre- quency (times /wk.)
1	Fitness walk	3.00	4.0		70–75	45	300	3
2	Fitness walk	3.25	4.0		70–75	49	325	3
3	Fitness walk	3.50	4.0		70–75	53	350	3
4	Fitness walk	3.50	4.5		75–80	47	350	3
5	Fitness walk	3.75	4.5		75–80	50	375	3
6	Fitness walk	4.00	4.5		75–80	53	400	3
7	Fitness walk	4.00	4.5	+	75–80	53	400	3
8	Fitness walk	4.00	4.5	+	75–80	53	>400‡	3
9	Fitness walk	4.00	4.5	+	75–80	53	>400‡	3
10	Fitness walk	4.00	4.5	+	75–80	53	>400‡	3
11	Fitness walk	4.00	4.5	+	75–80	53	>400‡	3
12	Fitness walk	4.00	4.5	+	75–80	53	>400‡	3
13	Fitness walk	4.00	4.5	+	75–80	53	>400‡	3
14	Fitness walk	4.00	4.5	+	75–80	53	>400‡	3
15	Fitness walk	4.00	4.5	+	75–80	53	>400‡	3
16	Fitness walk	4.00	4.5	+	75–80	53	>400‡	3
17	Fitness walk	4.00	4.5	+	75–80	53	>400‡	3
18	Fitness walk	4.00	4.5	+	75–80	53	>400‡	3
19	Fitness walk	4.00	4.5	+	75–80	53	>400‡	3
20	Fitness walk	4.00	4.5	+	75–80	53	>400‡	3

*The pace listed is only an approximation. The actual pace to be used is the one that keeps the heart rate as the appropriate % of max. listed.

**Weights (to upper body) or incline (hill walking) should be added as needed to keep heart rate in target zone (70–80% predicted maximum).

†Calorie expenditure is for an average 150-pound person. The number of calories burned will be slightly lower for lower body weight and slightly higher for higher body weight.

‡The exact number of calories burned will depend upon the amount of weight added.

Fitness Walking
Intermediate Maintenance Workout
Total time: 1 hour
Warm-up: 5–7 minutes of before-walk stretches (see fig. 19)
Aerobic workout:
    Mileage: 4.0
    Pace: 4.5 mph*
Heart rate: 70–80% of maximum
Calories burned: 400†
Cool-down: 10–12 minutes of after-walk stretches (see fig. 19)
Frequency: 3–6 times/week
Weekly mileage: 12–20

---

*The pace listed is only an approximation. The actual pace to be used is the one that keeps the heart rate at the appropriate % of max. listed.
†Calorie expenditure is for an average 150-pound person. The number of calories burned will be slightly lower for lower body weight and slightly higher for higher body weight.

Fitness Walking
Advanced Maintenance Workout
Total time: 1 hour
Warm-up: 5–7 minutes of before-walk stretches (see fig. 19)
Aerobic workout
    Mileage: 4.0
    Pace: 4.5 mph*
    Weight/incline: +†
Heart rate: 70–80% of maximum
Calories burned: >400‡
Cool-down: 10–12 minutes of after-walk stretches (see fig. 19)
Frequency: 3–5 times/week
Weekly mileage: 12–20

---

*The pace listed is only an approximation. The actual pace to be used is the one that keeps the heart rate at the appropriate % of max. listed.
†Weights (to upper body) or incline (hill walking) should be added as needed to keep heart rate in target zone (70–80% predicted maximum).
‡Calorie expenditure is for an average 150-pound person. The number of calories burned will be slightly lower for lower body weight and slightly higher for higher body weight. The exact number of calories burned will be determined by the amount of extra weight worn.

WALK/JOG/RUN

Jogging and running are excellent forms of aerobic exercise.

Several precautions will make your jogging and running program safer and more enjoyable. First, purchase a good pair of running shoes. Inadequate equipment is an invitation to injury. Most running specialty

FIG. 20

1
3 breaths.

2
2 breaths.
Alternate sides.

3
4 breaths.
Alternate sides.

4
5 breaths.

5
3 breaths.

(continued)

stores have knowledgeable salespeople who will help you select the right shoes for you. Second, start slow and build up through a careful progression. You'll notice that our starter, beginner and intermediate programs are all based on walking. If you fall into one of these categories it's important to build up your endurance with a walking program before attempting to tackle a more vigorous running program.

STRETCHING ROUTINE
FOR JOGGING AND RUNNING

In jogging or running, the muscles in the back of the legs do the most strenuous work of pushing backward to propel you forward. The hamstrings (in the back of the thighs) and the gastrocnemius muscles (in the calves) need the most stretching to reverse the shortening process. The most important joints to pay attention to are the ankles, knees and hips. The lower back takes a lot of pounding during runs and benefits from stretching as well. This stretching sequence (see fig. 20) covers all these areas as well as other muscle groups that support efficient running.

Go through the entire sequence, holding each stretch for at least the number of breaths indicated and alternating sides when required. Remember to breathe slowly and deeply from your belly. Consult chapter 3 for more information on the principles to keep in mind as you do this sequence. This 30-step routine should take you at least 17 minutes. Optimally, this stretching routine should be performed *before* the exercise session, and selected stretches should be done *after* the exercise.

6
Breathe out and
hold 3 secs.

7
Breathe in and
hold 3 secs.
Alternate 5 times
between #6 and #7.

8
5 circles with pelvis.

9
5 circles with pelvis.

10
5 breaths.

Walk/Jog/Run: Starter Program

Week	Exercise	Mileage	Pace* (mph)	Heart rate (% of max.)	Duration of workout (min.)	Calories burned†	Frequency (times/wk.)
1	Fitness walk	1.00	3.0	60	20	100	3
2	Fitness walk	1.00	3.0	60	20	100	3
3	Fitness walk	1.25	3.0	60	25	125	3
4	Fitness walk	1.25	3.0	60	25	125	3
5	Fitness walk	1.50	3.0	60	30	150	3
6	Fitness walk	1.50	3.5	65–70	26	150	3
7	Fitness walk	1.75	3.5	65–70	30	175	3
8	Fitness walk	1.75	3.5	65–70	30	175	3
9	Fitness walk	2.00	3.5	65–70	34	200	3
10	Fitness walk	2.00	3.75	65–70	32	200	3
11	Fitness walk	2.00	3.75	70–75	32	200	3
12	Fitness walk	2.25	3.75	70–75	36	225	3
13	Fitness walk	2.25	3.75	70–75	36	225	3
14	Fitness walk	2.50	3.75	70–75	40	250	3
15	Fitness walk	2.50	4.0	70–75	38	250	3
16	Fitness walk	2.50	4.0	70–75	38	250	3
17	Fitness walk	2.75	4.0	75–80	41	275	3
18	Fitness walk	2.75	4.0	75–80	41	275	3
19	Fitness walk	2.75	4.0	75–80	41	275	3
20	Fitness walk	2.75	4.0	75–80	41	275	3

*The pace listed is only an approximation. The actual pace to be used is the one that keeps the heart rate at the appropriate % of max. listed.
†Calorie expenditure is for an average 150-pound person. The number of calories burned will be slightly lower for lower body weight and slightly higher for higher body weight.

12 5 breaths.
Pull knee down across chest.
Alternate sides.

13 10 breaths.

14 5 breaths.

11 5 breaths. Alternate sides.

15 2 breaths. Alternate sides.

(continued)

Walk/Jog/Run: Beginner Program

Week	Exercise	Mileage	Pace* (mph)	Heart rate (% of max.)	Duration of workout (min.)	Calories burned†	Frequency (times/wk.)
1	Fitness walk	1.50	3.0	60–65	30	150	3
2	Fitness walk	1.50	3.0	60–65	30	150	3
3	Fitness walk	1.75	3.0	60–65	35	175	3
4	Fitness walk	1.75	3.0	60–65	35	175	3
5	Fitness walk	2.00	3.0	60–65	40	200	3
6	Fitness walk	2.00	3.0	60–65	40	200	3
7	Fitness walk	2.00	3.5	65–70	34	200	3
8	Fitness walk	2.25	3.5	65–70	38	225	3
9	Fitness walk	2.25	3.5	65–70	38	225	3
10	Fitness walk	2.50	3.5	65–70	43	250	3
11	Fitness walk	2.50	3.5	65–70	43	250	3
12	Fitness walk	2.50	3.5	65–70	43	250	3
13	Fitness walk	2.75	3.5	65–70	47	275	3
14	Fitness walk	2.75	3.5	65–70	47	275	3
15	Fitness walk	3.00	4.0	70–80	45	300	3
16	Fitness walk	3.00	4.0	70–80	45	300	3
17	Fitness walk	3.00	4.0	70–80	45	300	3
18	Fitness walk	3.00	4.0	70–80	45	300	3
19	Fitness walk	3.00	4.0	70–80	45	300	3
20	Fitness walk	3.00	4.0	70–80	45	300	3

*The pace listed is only an approximation. The actual pace to be used is the one that keeps the heart rate at the appropriate % of max. listed.
†Calorie expenditure is for an average 150-pound person. The number of calories burned will be slightly lower for lower body weight and slightly higher for higher body weight.

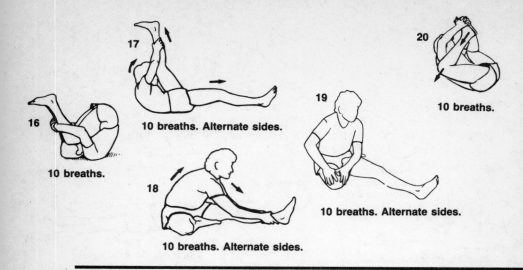

16 10 breaths.

17 10 breaths. Alternate sides.

18 10 breaths. Alternate sides.

19 10 breaths. Alternate sides.

20 10 breaths.

Walk/Jog/Run: Intermediate Program

Week	Exercise	Mileage	Pace* (mph)	Heart rate (% of max.)	Duration of workout (min.)	Calories burned†	Frequency (times/wk.)
1	Fitness walk	2.00	3.0	65–70	40	200	3
2	Fitness walk	2.25	3.0	65–70	45	225	3
3	Fitness walk	2.50	3.0	65–70	50	250	3
4	Fitness walk	2.50	3.0	65–70	50	250	3
5	Fitness walk	2.75	3.0	65–70	50	275	3
6	Fitness walk	2.75	3.5	70–75	47	275	3
7	Fitness walk	2.75	3.5	70–75	47	275	3
8	Fitness walk	2.75	3.5	70–75	47	275	3
9	Fitness walk	3.00	3.5	70–75	51	300	3
10	Fitness walk	3.00	3.5	70–75	51	300	3
11	Fitness walk	3.00	4.0	75–80	45	300	3
12	Fitness walk	3.00	4.0	75–80	45	300	3
13	Fitness walk	3.25	4.0	75–80	49	325	3
14	Fitness walk	3.25	4.0	75–80	49	325	3
15	Fitness walk	3.50	4.0	75–80	53	350	3
16	Fitness walk	3.50	4.5	75–80	47	350	3
17	Fitness walk	3.50	4.5	75–80	47	350	3
18	Fitness walk	3.50	4.5	75–80	47	350	3
19	Fitness walk	3.50	4.5	75–80	47	350	3
20	Fitness walk	3.50	4.5	75–80	47	350	3

*The pace listed is only an approximation. The actual pace to be used is the one that keeps the heart rate at the appropriate % of max. listed.

†Calorie expenditure is for an average 150-pound person. The number of calories burned will be slightly lower for lower body weight and slightly higher for higher body weight.

21 5 breaths. Alternate sides.

22 5 breaths.

23 5 breaths. Alternate sides.

24 5 breaths. Alternate sides.

25 5 breaths. Alternate sides.

(continued)

Walk/Jog/Run: Advanced Program

Week	Exercise	Mileage	Pace* (min./ (mile)	Heart rate (% of max.)	Duration of workout (min.)	Calories burned†	Frequency (times/wk.)
1	Jog/Run	2.00	8–10	70–75	16–20	200	3
2	Jog/Run	2.00	8–10	70–75	16–20	200	3
3	Jog/Run	2.25	8–10	70–75	18–23	225	3
4	Jog/Run	2.25	8–10	70–75	18–23	225	3
5	Jog/Run	2.50	8–10	70–75	20–25	250	3
6	Jog/Run	2.50	8–10	70–75	20–25	250	3
7	Jog/Run	3.00	8–10	70–75	24–30	300	3
8	Jog/Run	3.50	8–10	75–80	28–35	350	3
9	Jog/Run	3.50	7–10	75–80	25–35	350	3
10	Jog/Run	3.50	7–10	75–80	25–35	350	3
11	Jog/Run	4.00	7–10	75–80	28–40	400	3
12	Jog/Run	4.00	7–10	75–80	28–40	400	3
13	Jog/Run	4.00	7–10	75–80	28–40	400	3
14	Jog/Run	4.00	7–10	75–80	28–40	400	3
15	Jog/Run	4.50	7–10	75–80	28–40	450	3
16	Jog/Run	4.50	7–10	75–80	28–40	450	3
17	Jog/Run	4.50	7–10	75–80	28–40	450	3
18	Jog/Run	5.00	7–10	75–80	28–40	500	3
19	Jog/Run	5.00	7–10	75–80	28–40	500	3
20	Jog/Run	5.00	7–10	75–80	28–40	500	3

*Pace should be determined by the running speed that keeps the heart rate at 70–80% of predicted maximum.

†Calorie expenditure is for an average 150-pound person. The number of calories burned will be slightly lower for lower body weight and slightly higher for higher body weight.

26 10 breaths. Alternate sides.

27 5 breaths.

28 5 breaths. Alternate sides.

29 10 breaths. Alternate sides.

30 20 breaths.

Walk/Jog/Run: Expert Program

Week	Exercise	Mileage	Pace* (min./ (mile)	Heart rate (% of max.)	Duration of workout (min.)	Calories burned†	Frequency (times/wk.)
1	Jog/Run	3.00	8–10	75–80	24–30	300	3
2	Jog/Run	3.00	8–10	75–80	24–30	300	3
3	Jog/Run	3.50	8–10	75–80	28–35	350	3
4	Jog/Run	4.00	8–10	75–80	32–40	400	3
5	Jog/Run	4.00	7–10	75–80	28–40	400	3
6	Jog/Run	4.00	7–10	75–80	28–40	400	3
7	Jog/Run	4.50	7–10	75–80	31–45	450	3
8	Jog/Run	4.50	7–10	75–80	31–45	450	3
9	Jog/Run	4.50	7–10	75–80	31–45	450	3
10	Jog/Run	5.00	7–10	75–80	35–50	500	3
11	Jog/Run	5.00	7–10	75–80	35–50	500	3
12	Jog/Run	5.00	7–10	75–80	35–50	500	3
13	Jog/Run	5.50	7–10	75–80	38–55	550	3
14	Jog/Run	5.50	7–10	75–80	38–55	550	3
15	Jog/Run	5.50	7–10	75–80	38–55	550	3
16	Jog/Run	6.00	7–10	75–80	42–60	600	3
17	Jog/Run	6.00	7–10	75–80	42–60	600	3
18	Jog/Run	6.00	7–10	75–80	42–60	600	3
19	Jog/Run	6.00	7–10	75–80	42–60	600	3
20	Jog/Run	6.00	7–10	75–80	42–60	600	3

*Pace should be determined by the running speed that keeps the heart rate at 70–80% of predicted maximum.
†Calorie expenditure is for an average 150-pound person. The number of calories burned will be slightly lower for lower body weight and slightly higher for higher body weight.

Walk/Jog/Run
Intermediate Maintenance Workout
Total time: 35–60 minutes
Warm-up: 10–12 minutes of before-run stretches (see fig. 20)
Aerobic workout:
    Mileage: 4–5
    Pace: 7–10 minutes/mile*
Heart rate: 70–80% of maximum
Calories burned: 400–500†
Cool-down: 10–12 minutes of after-run stretches (see fig. 20)
Frequency: 3 times/week
Weekly mileage: 12–15

---

*Pace should be determined by the running speed that keeps heart rate at 70–80% of predicted maximum.
†Calorie expenditure is for an average 150-pound person. The number of calories burned will be slightly lower for lower body weight and slightly higher for higher body weight.

Walk/Jog/Run
Advanced Maintenance Workout
Total time: 45–70 minutes
Warm-up: 10–12 minutes of before-run stretches (see fig. 20)
Aerobic workout:
    Mileage: 5–6
    Pace: 7–10 minutes/mile*
Heart rate: 70–80% of maximum
Calories burned: 500–600†
Cool-down: 10–12 minutes of after-run stretches (see fig. 20)
Frequency: 3 times/week
Weekly mileage: 15–18

---

*Pace should be determined by the running speed that keeps heart rate at 70–80% of predicted maximum.
†Calorie expenditure is for an average 150-pound person. The number of calories burned will be slightly lower for lower body weight and slightly higher for higher body weight.

SWIMMING

Swimming is an excellent sport to build up aerobic capacity. Swimming provides conditioning for both arms and legs and is particularly beneficial for individuals with orthopedic problems. Many recreational facilities now set aside specific times at their pools for lap swimming.

FIG. 21

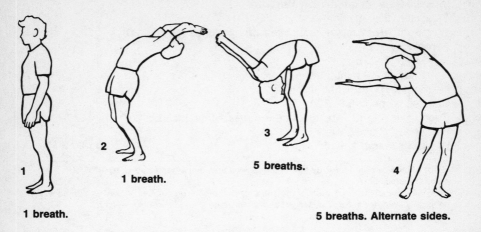

1

1 breath.

2

1 breath.

3

5 breaths.

4

5 breaths. Alternate sides.

STRETCHING ROUTINE FOR SWIMMING

Swimming, of course, is an exercise that gives you no jarring or pounding, so stress on the joints is minimal. Depending on your stroke, you will be using different muscle groups in both the upper body and the lower body. The sequence recommended here (see fig. 21) covers major muscle groups used in the crawl, the breaststroke and the backstroke. For the crawl, the areas in most need of stretching are the chest (pectorals), shoulders (deltoids), back (latissimus) and arms (triceps), as well as the lower back and the back of the legs.

Go through the entire sequence, holding each stretch for at least the number of breaths indicated and alternating sides when required. Remember to breathe slowly and deeply from your belly, and feel free to rest between stretches for as long as you like. Consult chapter 3 for more information on the principles to keep in mind as you do this sequence. This 25-step routine should take you at least 12 minutes. Optimally, this stretching routine should be performed *before* your swimming workout, and selected stretches should be done *after* your workout.

5 breaths. Alternate sides.

5
Breathe out and hold 3 secs.

6
Breathe in and hold 3 secs. Alternate between 5 times #5 and #6.

7

8

5 breaths. Alternate sides.

(continued)

Swimming: Starter Program

Week	Exercise	Aerobic set (yds.)	Heart rate (% of max.)	Calories burned*	Frequency (times/wk.)
1	Swim	100†	60	21	3
2	Swim	125	60	26	3
3	Swim	150	60	31	3
4	Swim	175	60	36	3
5	Swim	200	60	42	3
6	Swim	200	65–70	42	3
7	Swim	250	65–70	52	3
8	Swim	275	65–70	57	3
9	Swim	300	65–70	64	3
10	Swim	350	65–70	74	3
11	Swim	400‡	70–75	84	3
12	Swim	450	70–75	94	3
13	Swim	500	70–75	106	3
14	Swim	600	70–75	127	3
15	Swim	700	70–75	148	3
16	Swim	800	75–80	168	3
17	Swim	900	75–80	189	3
18	Swim	900	75–80	189	3
19	Swim	1000	75–80	210	3
20	Swim	1000	75–80	210	3

*Assumes a 150-pound individual swimming freestyle at 50 yards/minute.
†Rest 30 seconds after every 25 yards and 1 minute after every 50 yards.
‡Rest 30 seconds after every 50 yards and 1 minute after every 100 yards.

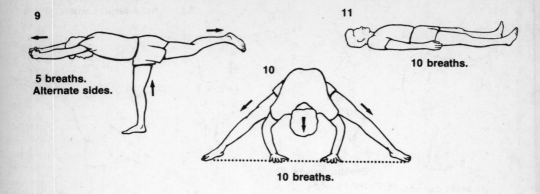

9 5 breaths. Alternate sides.

10 10 breaths.

11 10 breaths.

Swimming: Beginner Program

Week	Exercise	Aerobic set (yds.)	Heart rate (% of max.)	Calories burned*	Frequency (times/wk.)
1	Swim	100†	60–65	21	3
2	Swim	125	60–65	26	3
3	Swim	150	60–65	31	3
4	Swim	200	60–65	42	3
5	Swim	250	60–65	53	3
6	Swim	300	65–70	64	3
7	Swim	350	65–70	74	3
8	Swim	400‡	65–70	84	3
9	Swim	450	65–70	94	3
10	Swim	500	65–70	106	3
11	Swim	550	70–75	116	3
12	Swim	600	70–75	127	3
13	Swim	650	70–75	137	3
14	Swim	700	70–75	148	3
15	Swim	800	70–75	168	3
16	Swim	900	75–80	189	3
17	Swim	1000	75–80	210	3
18	Swim	1100	75–80	231	3
19	Swim	1200	75–80	252	3
20	Swim	1200	75–80	252	3

*Assumes a 150-pound individual swimming freestyle at 50 yards/minute.
†Rest 30 seconds after every 25 yards and 1 minute after every 50 yards.
‡Rest 30 seconds after every 50 yards and 1 minute after every 100 yards.

12

10 breaths.

13

10 breaths.

14

Breathe out and hold 3 secs.

15

Breathe in and hold 3 secs. Alternate 5 times between #14 and #15.

(continued)

Swimming: Intermediate Program

Week	Exercise	Aerobic set (yds.)	Heart rate (% of max.)	Calories burned*	Frequency (times/wk.)
1	Swim	150†	65–70	31	3
2	Swim	200	65–70	42	3
3	Swim	250	65–70	52	3
4	Swim	300	65–70	64	3
5	Swim	350	65–70	74	3
6	Swim	400‡	70–75	84	3
7	Swim	450	70–75	94	3
8	Swim	500	70–75	106	3
9	Swim	550	70–75	116	3
10	Swim	600	70–75	127	3
11	Swim	650	75–80	137	3
12	Swim	700	75–80	148	3
13	Swim	800	75–80	168	3
14	Swim	900	75–80	189	3
15	Swim	1000	75–80	210	3
16	Swim	1100	75–80	231	3
17	Swim	1200	75–80	252	3
18	Swim	1300	75–80	274	3
19	Swim	1500	75–80	316	3
20	Swim	1500	75–80	316	3

*Assumes a 150-pound individual swimming freestyle at 50 yards/minute.
†Rest 30 seconds after every 25 yards and 1 minute after every 50 yards.
‡Rest 30 seconds after every 50 yards and 1 minute after every 100 yards.

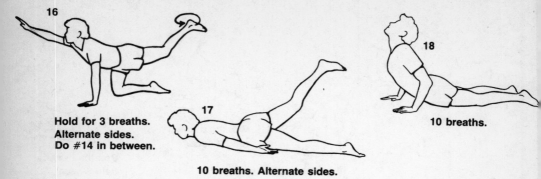

**Hold for 3 breaths.
Alternate sides.
Do #14 in between.**

10 breaths. Alternate sides.

10 breaths.

Swimming: Advanced Program

Week	Exercise	Aerobic set (yds.)	Heart rate (% of max.)	Calories burned*	Frequency (times/wk.)
1	Swim	250†	70–75	52	3
2	Swim	300	70–74	64	3
3	Swim	350	70–75	74	3
4	Swim	400	70–75	84	3
5	Swim	450	70–75	94	3
6	Swim	500	75–80	106	3
7	Swim	550	75–80	116	3
8	Swim	600‡	75–80	127	3
9	Swim	650	75–80	137	3
10	Swim	700	75–80	148	3
11	Swim	800	75–80	168	3
12	Swim	900	75–80	189	3
13	Swim	1000	75–80	210	3
14	Swim	1100	75–80	231	3
15	Swim	1200	75–80	252	3
16	Swim	1300	75–80	274	3
17	Swim	1400	75–80	295	3
18	Swim	1500	75–80	316	3
19	Swim	1700	75–80	358	3
20	Swim	1700	75–80	358	3

*Assumes a 150-pound individual swimming freestyle at 50 yards/minute.
†Rest 30 seconds after every 50 yards and 1 minute after every 100 yards.
‡Make an effort to swim continuously, periodically monitoring pulse to assure that it is in the target zone.

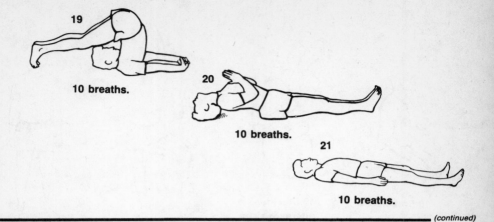

19 10 breaths.

20 10 breaths.

21 10 breaths.

(continued)

Swimming: Expert Program

Week	Exercise	Aerobic set (yds.)	Heart rate (% of max.)	Calories burned*	Frequency (times/wk.)
1	Swim	400†	70–75	84	3
2	Swim	450	70–75	94	3
3	Swim	500	70–75	106	3
4	Swim	550	70–75	116	3
5	Swim	600‡	70–75	127	3
6	Swim	650	75–80	137	3
7	Swim	700	75–80	148	3
8	Swim	750	75–80	158	3
9	Swim	800	75–80	168	3
10	Swim	900	75–80	189	3
11	Swim	1000	75–80	210	3
12	Swim	1100	75–80	231	3
13	Swim	1200	75–80	252	3
14	Swim	1300	75–80	274	3
15	Swim	1400	75–80	295	3
16	Swim	1500	75–80	316	3
17	Swim	1600	75–80	337	3
18	Swim	1800	75–80	379	3
19	Swim	2000	75–80	421	3
20	Swim	2000	75–80	421	3

*Assumes a 150-pound individual swimming freestyle at 50 yards/minute.
†Rest 30 seconds after every 100 yards and 1 minute after every 100 yards.
‡Make an effort to swim continuously, periodically monitoring pulse to assure that it is in the target zone.

22

10 breaths.

23

**10 breaths.
Alternate sides.**

24

**10 breaths.
Alternate sides.**

25

10 breaths.

Swimming: Intermediate Maintenance Workout
Total distance: 1700 yards
Warm-up
    Out of pool: 8–10 minutes of before-swim stretches (see fig. 21)
    In pool: 100 yards easy swim (your choice of stroke)
Aerobic set
    Distance: 1500 yards (vary strokes: crawl, breaststroke, backstroke,
    butterfly)*
Heart rate: 70–80% of maximum†
Calories burned: 358‡
Cool-down
    In pool: 100 yards easy swim (your choice of stroke)
    On land: 8–10 minutes of after-swim stretches (see fig. 21)
Frequency: 3 times/week

---

*Make an effort to swim continuously, periodically monitoring pulse to assure that it is in the
target zone.
†Pace should be determined by the swimming speed that maintains heart rate at 70–80% of
predicted maximum.
‡Assumes a 150-pound individual swimming freestyle at 50 yards/minute.

Swimming
Advanced Maintenance Workout
Total distance: 2220 yards
Warm-up
> On land: 8–10 minutes of before-swim stretches (see fig. 21)
> In pool: 200 yards easy swim (your choice of stroke)

Aerobic set
> Distance: 1800 yards (vary strokes: crawl, breaststroke, backstroke, butterfly)*

Heart rate: 70–80% of maximum†
Calories burned: 463‡
Cool-down
> In pool: 200 yards easy swim (your choice of stroke)
> On land: 8–10 minutes of after-swim stretches (see fig. 21)

Frequency: 3 times/week

---

*Make an effort to swim continuously, periodically monitoring pulse to assure that it is in the target zone.
†Pace should be determined by the swimming speed that maintains heart rate at 70–80% of predicted maximum.
‡Assumes a 150-pound individual swimming freestyle at 50 yards/minute.

CYCLING

Cycling is a very good form of aerobic conditioning which is increasing in popularity. The most important equipment decision you will need to make if you choose this activity is, of course, which bicycle is best for you. If it has been many years since you rode a bicycle, you'll be amazed at all the technical advances which have been made. We recommend that you purchase your bicycle from a specialty shop dealing only in bicycles. A knowledgeable salesperson can help guide you through the various options to choose the right bicycle for you.

Remember, when you cycle to improve your aerobic capacity, you need to monitor your heart rate to get it up into the recommended training zone. In our experience we have seen that most people do not exercise vigorously enough while cycling to derive the maximum benefit.

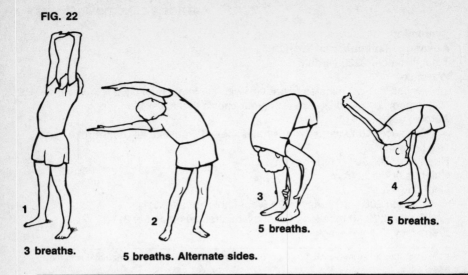

FIG. 22

1
3 breaths.

2
5 breaths. Alternate sides.

3
5 breaths.

4
5 breaths.

STRETCHING ROUTINE FOR CYCLING

In cycling, the muscle groups exerting the greatest force are the quadriceps (in the front of the thighs) and the calf muscles in the lower legs which help push the pedal down as the leg straightens against resistance. If you use toe clips, you also will be pulling up on the pedals, primarily with the hamstrings and the hip flexors. Arm and shoulder muscles are also involved in strenuous cycling. Cycling tends to introduce tension into the back, shoulders, arms and neck from maintaining the crouched position with the neck hyperextended for long periods of time and also from the shock of bumps. For these reasons, a comprehensive stretching routine for cycling (see fig. 22) is essential to maintain enjoyment as well as fitness. We recommend that you do shoulder shrugs (fig. 22, #9) and neck rolls (fig. 22, #10) right before cycling, as well as a lower-back stretch and a quadriceps stretch.

Go through the entire sequence, holding each stretch for at least the number of breaths indicated and alternating sides when required. Remember to breathe slowly and deeply from your belly and feel free to rest between stretches for as long as you like. Consult chapter 3 for more information on the principles to keep in mind as you do this sequence. This 27-step routine should take you at least 17 minutes. Optimally, this stretching routine should be performed *before* cycling, and selected stretches should be done *after* cycling.

5
5 breaths.

6
10 breaths.

7

8 breaths.

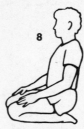

8
10 breaths.

9
10 rotations
each direction.

(continued)

Cycling: Starter Program

Week	Exercise	Distance (miles)	Approx-imate pace* (min./mile)	Heart rate (% of max.)	Approx-imate duration of workout (min.)	Calories burned†	Fre-quency (times/wk.)
1	Cycle	2	8	60	16:00	80	3
2	Cycle	2	7.5	60	15:00	80	3
3	Cycle	2.5	8	60	20:00	100	3
4	Cycle	2.5	7.5	60	18:45	100	3
5	Cycle	3	8	60	24:00	120	3
6	Cycle	3	7.5	65–70	22:30	120	3
7	Cycle	3	7.5	65–70	22:30	120	3
8	Cycle	3.5	8	65–70	28:00	140	3
9	Cycle	3.5	7.5	65–70	26:15	140	3
10	Cycle	3.5	7.5	65–70	26:15	140	3
11	Cycle	4	8	70–75	32:00	160	3
12	Cycle	4	7.5	70–75	30:00	160	3
13	Cycle	4	7.5	70–75	30:00	160	3
14	Cycle	4.5	8	70–75	36:00	180	3
15	Cycle	4.5	7.5	75–80	33:45	180	3
16	Cycle	4.5	7.5	75–80	33:45	180	3
17	Cycle	5	8	75–80	40:00	200	3
18	Cycle	5	7.5	75–80	37:30	200	3
19	Cycle	5	7.5	75–80	37:30	200	3
20	Cycle	5	7.5	75–80	37:30	200	3

*The approximate pace is intended only to serve as a guideline. The exact pace will be determined by the speed required to attain the percentage of maximum heart rate indicated.
†Assumes cycling on level ground at approximate pace indicated.

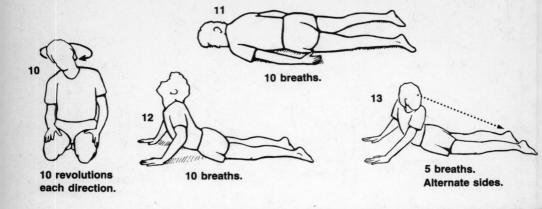

10 — 10 revolutions each direction.

11 — 10 breaths.

12 — 10 breaths.

13 — 5 breaths. Alternate sides.

Cycling: Beginner Program

Week	Exercise	Distance (miles)	Approximate pace* (min./mile)	Heart rate (% of max.)	Approximate duration of workout (min.)	Calories burned†	Frequency (times/wk.)
1	Cycle	3	7.5	60	22:30	120	3
2	Cycle	3	7	60	21:00	120	3
3	Cycle	3.5	7.5	60	26:15	135	3
4	Cycle	3.5	7	60	22:30	135	3
5	Cycle	3.5	7	60	22:30	135	3
6	Cycle	4	7.5	65–70	30:00	150	3
7	Cycle	4	7	65–70	28:00	150	3
8	Cycle	4.5	7.5	65–70	33:45	165	3
9	Cycle	4.5	7	65–70	31:30	165	3
10	Cycle	5	7.5	65–70	37:30	180	3
11	Cycle	5	7	70–75	35:00	180	3
12	Cycle	5.5	7.5	70–75	41:15	195	3
13	Cycle	5.5	7	70–75	38:30	195	3
14	Cycle	5.5	7	70–75	38:30	195	3
15	Cycle	6	7.5	70–75	45:00	220	3
16	Cycle	6	7	75–80	42:00	220	3
17	Cycle	6	7	75–80	42:00	220	3
18	Cycle	6.5	7.5	75–80	48:45	235	3
19	Cycle	6.5	7	75–80	45:30	235	3
20	Cycle	6.5	7	75–80	45:30	235	3

*The approximate pace is intended only to serve as a guideline. The exact pace will be determined by the speed required to attain the percentage of maximum heart rate indicated.
†Assumes cycling on level ground at approximate pace indicated.

14

8 breaths.

15

10 breaths.
Alternate sides.

16

10 breaths.
Alternate sides.

17

8 breaths.
Alternate sides.

18

15 breaths.

(continued)

Cycling: Intermediate Program

Week	Exercise	Distance (miles)	Approximate pace* (min./mile)	Heart rate (% of max.)	Approximate duration of workout (min.)	Calories burned†	Frequency (times/wk.)
1	Cycle	4	7	65–70	28:00	156	3
2	Cycle	4	6.5	65–70	26:00	156	3
2	Cycle	4	6.5	65–70	26:00	156	3
3	Cycle	4.5	7	65–70	31:30	172	3
4	Cycle	4.5	6.5	65–70	29:15	172	3
5	Cycle	4.5	6.5	65–70	29:15	172	3
6	Cycle	5	7	70–75	35:00	182	3
7	Cycle	5	6.5	70–75	32:30	182	3
8	Cycle	5	6.5	70–75	32:30	182	3
9	Cycle	5.5	6.5	70–75	35:45	203	3
10	Cycle	5.5	6.5	75–80	35:45	203	3
11	Cycle	5.5	6.5	75–80	35:45	203	3
12	Cycle	6	7	75–80	42:00	218	3
13	Cycle	6	6.5	75–80	39:00	218	3
14	Cycle	6	6.5	75–80	39:00	218	3
15	Cycle	6.5	6.5	75–80	42:15	234	3
16	Cycle	6.5	6.5	75–80	42:15	234	3
17	Cycle	6.5	6.5	75–80	42:15	234	3
18	Cycle	7.5	6.5	75–80	48:45	266	3
19	Cycle	7.5	6.5	75–80	48:45	266	3
20	Cycle	7.5	6.5	75–80	48:45	226	3

*The approximate pace is intended only to serve as a guideline. The exact pace will be determined by the speed required to attain the percentage of maximum heart rate indicated.
†Assumes cycling on level ground at approximate pace indicated.

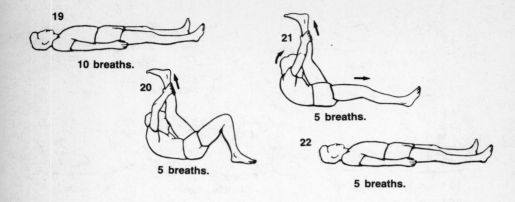

19 10 breaths.

20 5 breaths.

21 5 breaths.

22 5 breaths.

Cycling
Advanced Program

Week	Exercise	Distance (miles)	Approx-imate pace* (min./mile)	Heart rate (% of max.)	Approx-imate duration of workout (min.)	Calories burned†	Fre-quency (times/wk.)
1	Cycle	5	6	70–75	30	192	3
2	Cycle	5	6	70–75	30	192	3
3	Cycle	5.5	6	70–75	33	211	3
4	Cycle	5.5	6	70–75	33	211	3
5	Cycle	5.5	6	70–75	33	211	3
6	Cycle	6	6	70–75	36	230	3
7	Cycle	6	6	70–75	36	230	3
8	Cycle	6	6	70–75	36	230	3
9	Cycle	6.5	6	70–75	39	249	3
10	Cycle	6.5	6	70–75	39	249	3
11	Cycle	6.5	6	70–75	39	249	3
12	Cycle	7	6	75–80	42	268	3
13	Cycle	7	6	75–80	42	268	3
14	Cycle	7	6	75–80	42	268	3
15	Cycle	7.5	6	75–80	45	287	3
16	Cycle	7.5	6	75–80	45	287	3
17	Cycle	7.5	6	75–80	45	287	3
18	Cycle	8	6	75–80	48	306	3
19	Cycle	8	6	75–80	48	306	3
20	Cycle	8	6	75–80	48	306	3

*The approximate pace is intended only to serve as a guideline. The exact pace will be determined by the speed required to attain the percentage of maximum heart rate indicated.
†Assumes cycling on level ground at approximate pace indicated.

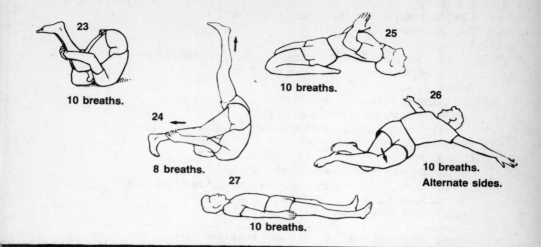

23 10 breaths.

24 8 breaths.

25 10 breaths.

26 10 breaths. Alternate sides.

27 10 breaths.

Cycling: Expert Program

Week	Exercise	Distance (miles)	Approximate pace* (min./mile)	Heart rate (% of max.)	Approximate duration of workout (min.)	Calories burned†	Frequency (times/wk.)
1	Cycle	6	5	70–75	30:00	261	3
2	Cycle	6	5	70–75	30:00	261	3
3	Cycle	6	5	70–75	30:00	261	3
4	Cycle	6.5	5	70–75	32:30	283	3
5	Cycle	6.5	5	70–75	32:30	283	3
6	Cycle	6.5	5	75–80	32:30	283	3
7	Cycle	7	5	75–80	35:00	305	3
8	Cycle	7	5	75–80	35:00	305	3
9	Cycle	7	5	75–80	35:00	305	3
10	Cycle	7.5	5	75–80	37:30	327	3
11	Cycle	7.5	5	75–80	37:30	327	3
12	Cycle	7.5	5	75–80	37:30	327	3
13	Cycle	8	5	75–80	40:00	349	3
14	Cycle	8	5	75–80	40:00	349	3
15	Cycle	8	5	75–80	40:00	349	3
16	Cycle	8.5	5	75–80	42:30	371	3
17	Cycle	8.5	5	75–80	42:30	371	3
18	Cycle	8.5	5	75–80	42:30	371	3
19	Cycle	9	5	75–80	45:00	393	3
20	Cycle	9	5	75–80	45:00	393	3

*The approximate pace is intended only to serve as a guideline. The exact pace will be determined by the speed required to attain the percentage of maximum heart rate indicated.
†Assumes cycling on level ground at approximate pace indicated.

Cycling: Intermediate Maintenance Workout

Total distance: 8 miles
Warm-up
    Stretching: 8–10 minutes of before-cycling stretches (see fig. 22)
    Cycling warm-up: ½ mile (easy pedaling)
Aerobic workout
    Distance: 7 miles
    Approximate pace: 6 minutes/mile*
    Approximate duration of workout: 42 minutes
Heart rate: 75–80% of maximum
Cool-down
    Cycling cool-down: ½ mile (easy pedaling)
    Stretching: 8–10 minutes of after-cycling stretches (see fig. 22)
Calories burned: 349†
Frequency: 3 times/week

---

*The approximate pace is intended only to serve as a guideline. The exact pace will be determined by the speed required to attain the percentage of maximum heart rate indicated.
†Assumes cycling on level ground at approximate pace indicated.

Cycling: Advanced Maintenance Workout

Total distance: 9 miles
Warm-up
    Stretching: 8–10 minutes of before-cycling stretches (see fig. 22)
    Cycling warm-up: ½ mile (easy pedaling)
Aerobic workout
    Distance: 8 miles
    Approximate pace: 5 minutes/mile*
    Approximate duration of workout: 40 minutes
Heart rate: 75–80% of maximum
Cool-down
    Cycling cool-down: ½ mile (easy pedaling)
    Stretching: 8–10 minutes of after-cycling stretches (see fig. 22)
Calories burned: 393†
Frequency: 3 times/week

---

*The approximate pace is intended only to serve as a guideline. The exact pace will be determined by the speed required to attain the percentage of maximum heart rate indicated.
†Assumes cycling on level ground at approximate pace indicated.

STATIONARY CYCLING

Stationary cycling is an excellent addition to other forms of aerobic conditioning. We often use it in fitness walking or running-jogging programs as an alternative activity in bad weather or just a change of pace. It is also an excellent conditioner for those with orthopedic problems or rehabilitating from injury. Many good stationary cycles are now commercially available.

STRETCHING ROUTINE FOR STATIONARY CYCLING

In stationary cycling, the muscle groups exerting the greatest force are the quadriceps (in the front of the thighs) and the calf muscles which help push the pedal down as the leg straightens against resistance. If you use toe clips, you also will be pulling up primarily with the hamstrings, and the hip flexors. Arm, shoulder and neck muscles are not much involved, but we suggest you do the same comprehensive stretching routine given for cycling (see fig. 22). Go through the entire sequence, holding each stretch for at least the number of breaths indicated and alternating sides when required. Breathe slowly and deeply from your belly and feel free to rest between stretches for as long as you like. See chapter 3 for principles to keep in mind as you do this sequence. The 27-step routine should take you at least 17 minutes. Optimally, this routine should be performed *before* stationary cycling, and selected stretches should be done *afterward*.

Stationary Cycling: Starter Program

Week	Exercise	RPM	Heart rate* (% of max.)	Duration of workout (min.)	Calories burned†	Frequency (times/wk.)
1	Stationary cycle	50	60	16	90	3
2	Stationary cycle	50	60	16	90	3
3	Stationary cycle	50	60	18	100	3
4	Stationary cycle	50	60	18	100	3
5	Stationary cycle	50	60	20	112	3
6	Stationary cycle	50	65–70	20	115	3
7	Stationary cycle	50	65–70	22	125	3
8	Stationary cycle	60	65–70	22	147	3
9	Stationary cycle	60	65–70	24	162	3
10	Stationary cycle	60	65–70	24	162	3
11	Stationary cycle	60	70–75	26	180	3
12	Stationary cycle	60	70–75	26	180	3
13	Stationary cycle	60	70–75	28	195	3
14	Stationary cycle	60	70–75	28	195	3
15	Stationary cycle	60	70–75	30	210	3
16	Stationary cycle	60	75–80	30	215	3
17	Stationary cycle	60	75–80	32	225	3
18	Stationary cycle	60	75–80	32	225	3
19	Stationary cycle	60	75–80	34	235	3
20	Stationary cycle	60	75–80	34	235	3

*Set bicycle resistance to keep the heart rate at the appropriate % of max. as listed.
†Calorie expenditure is for an average 150-pound person. The number of calories burned will be slightly lower for lower body weight and slightly higher for higher body weight.

Stationary Cycling: Beginner Program

Week	Exercise	RPM	Heart rate* (% of max.)	Duration of workout (min.)	Calories burned†	Frequency (times/wk.)
1	Stationary cycle	50	60	18	100	3
2	Stationary cycle	50	60	18	100	3
3	Stationary cycle	50	60	20	112	3
4	Stationary cycle	50	60	20	112	3
5	Stationary cycle	50	60	22	120	3
6	Stationary cycle	50	65	22	125	3
7	Stationary cycle	50	65–70	24	135	3
8	Stationary cycle	60	65–70	24	162	3
9	Stationary cycle	60	65–70	26	174	3
10	Stationary cycle	60	65–70	26	174	3
11	Stationary cycle	60	70–75	28	195	3
12	Stationary cycle	60	70–75	28	195	3
13	Stationary cycle	60	70–75	30	210	3
14	Stationary cycle	60	70–75	30	210	3
15	Stationary cycle	60	70–75	32	213	3
16	Stationary cycle	60	75–80	32	225	3
17	Stationary cycle	60	75–80	34	235	3
18	Stationary cycle	60	75–80	34	235	3
19	Stationary cycle	60	75–80	36	245	3
20	Stationary cycle	60	75–80	36	245	3

*Set bicycle resistance to keep the heart rate at the appropriate % of max. as listed.
†Calorie expenditure is for an average 150-pound person. The number of calories burned will be slightly lower for lower body weight and slightly higher for higher body weight.

Stationary Cycling: Intermediate Program

Week	Exercise	RPM	Heart rate* (% of max.)	Duration of workout (min.)	Calories burned†	Frequency (times/wk.)
1	Stationary cycle	50	65–70	20	115	3
2	Stationary cycle	50	65–70	20	115	3
3	Stationary cycle	50	65–70	22	130	3
4	Stationary cycle	50	65–70	22	130	3
5	Stationary cycle	50	65–70	24	140	3
6	Stationary cycle	60	70–75	24	165	3
7	Stationary cycle	60	70–75	26	175	3
8	Stationary cycle	60	70–75	26	175	3
9	Stationary cycle	60	70–75	28	200	3
10	Stationary cycle	60	70–75	28	200	3
11	Stationary cycle	60	75–80	30	210	3
12	Stationary cycle	60	75–80	30	210	3
13	Stationary cycle	60	75–80	32	230	3
14	Stationary cycle	60	75–80	32	230	3
15	Stationary cycle	60	75–80	34	240	3
16	Stationary cycle	70	75–80	34	270	3
17	Stationary cycle	70	75–80	36	282	3
18	Stationary cycle	70	75–80	36	282	3
19	Stationary cycle	70	75–80	38	297	3
20	Stationary cycle	70	75–80	38	297	3

*Set bicycle resistance to keep the heart rate at the appropriate % of max. as listed.

†Calorie expenditure is for an average 150-pound person. The number of calories burned will be slightly lower for lower body weight and slightly higher for higher body weight.

Stationary Cycling: Advanced Program

Week	Exercise	RPM	Heart rate* (% of max.)	Duration of workout (min.)	Calories burned†	Frequency (times/wk.)
1	Stationary cycle	60	70–75	22	160	3
2	Stationary cycle	60	70–75	22	160	3
3	Stationary cycle	60	70–75	24	175	3
4	Stationary cycle	60	70–75	24	175	3
5	Stationary cycle	60	70–75	26	190	3
6	Stationary cycle	60	70–75	26	190	3
7	Stationary cycle	60	70–75	28	205	3
8	Stationary cycle	60	70–75	28	205	3
9	Stationary cycle	60	70–75	30	215	3
10	Stationary cycle	60	70–75	30	215	3
11	Stationary cycle	70	75–80	32	250	3
12	Stationary cycle	70	75–80	32	250	3
13	Stationary cycle	70	75–80	34	270	3
14	Stationary cycle	70	75–80	34	270	3
15	Stationary cycle	70	75–80	36	290	3
16	Stationary cycle	70	75–80	36	290	3
17	Stationary cycle	70	75–80	38	310	3
18	Stationary cycle	70	75–80	38	310	3
19	Stationary cycle	70	75–80	40	330	3
20	Stationary cycle	70	75–80	40	330	3

*Set bicycle resistance to keep the heart rate at the appropriate % of max. as listed.
†Calorie expenditure is for an average 150-pound person. The number of calories burned will be slightly lower for lower body weight and slightly higher for higher body weight.

Stationary Cycle
Intermediate Maintenance Workout
Warm-up
>Stretching: 8–10 minutes of before-cycling stretches (see fig. 22)
>Cycle warm-up: 3 minutes (easy pedaling)

Aerobic workout
>RPM: 70
>Time: 36 minutes

Heart rate: 75–80% of maximum
Cool-down
>Cycling cool-down: 3 minutes (easy pedaling)
>Stretching: 8–10 minutes of after-cycling stretches (see fig. 22)

Calories burned: 295
Frequency: 3 times/week

Stationary Cycling: Expert Program

Week	Exercise	RPM	Heart rate* (% of max.)	Duration of workout (min.)	Calories burned†	Frequency (times/wk.)
1	Stationary cycle	60	70–75	24	180	3
2	Stationary cycle	60	70–75	24	180	3
3	Stationary cycle	60	70–75	26	195	3
4	Stationary cycle	60	70–75	26	195	3
5	Stationary cycle	60	70–75	28	210	3
6	Stationary cycle	70	75–80	28	219	3
7	Stationary cycle	70	75–80	30	240	3
8	Stationary cycle	70	75–80	30	240	3
9	Stationary cycle	70	75–80	32	255	3
10	Stationary cycle	70	75–80	32	255	3
11	Stationary cycle	70	75–80	34	275	3
12	Stationary cycle	70	75–80	34	275	3
13	Stationary cycle	70	75–80	36	295	3
14	Stationary cycle	70	75–80	36	295	3
15	Stationary cycle	70	75–80	38	315	3
16	Stationary cycle	80	75–80	38	340	3
17	Stationary cycle	80	75–80	40	360	3
18	Stationary cycle	80	75–80	40	360	3
19	Stationary cycle	80	75–80	42	380	3
20	Stationary cycle	80	75–80	42	380	3

*Set bicycle resistance to keep the heart rate at the appropriate % of max. as listed.
†Calorie expenditure is for an average 150-pound person. The number of calories burned will be slightly lower for lower body weight and slightly higher for higher body weight.

Stationary Cycle
Advanced Maintenance Workout
Warm-up
    Stretching: 8–10 minutes of before-cycling stretches (see fig. 22)
    Cycle warm-up: 3 minutes (easy pedaling)
Aerobic workout
    RPM: 70
    Time: 40 minutes:
Heart rate: 75–80% of maximum
Cool-down
    Cycling cool-down: 3 minutes (easy pedaling)
    Stretching: 8–10 minutes of after-cycling stretches (see fig. 22)
Calories burned: 360
Frequency: 3 times/week

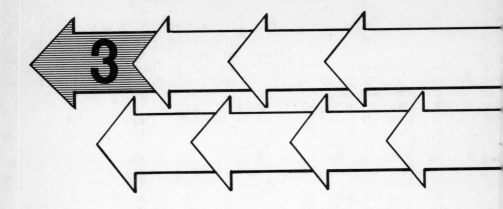

Flexibility and stretching constitute an essential component of total fitness for top performance. Until recently, flexibility was not considered an important dimension of fitness, and stretching usually took a back seat to other aspects of physical training, if it was included at all. This attitude is changing, as more fitness-minded physicians and individuals realize that exercise can lead to muscle tightness as it builds muscle strength. In this process the muscles actually shorten their resting length. If this is not reversed, an exercise program can lead to greater and greater muscle tightness, or what is called the overuse syndrome. In its extreme form, it can cause muscle strain and injury. Since some muscle groups experience overuse and others do not, depending on which form of exercise you are pursuing, your body can easily develop imbalances in both strength and flexibility. For this reason, it is very important that you take steps to reestablish balance in your body by stretching. The specific muscle groups that become the tightest because of your exercise program obviously have the most need of being stretched. But it is also important that you do at least a little work to *strengthen* those muscle groups which are not used in a particular sport and which can become weaker through disuse and through pounding (i.e., the lower back and abdominal muscles for runners and cyclists). For these reasons, we have given you specific stretching sequences to be followed for different sports you may be pursuing. As you will see when you do them, a good deal of muscle strengthening takes place during many of the stretching exercises. Often while one part of your body is being stretched other regions are being strengthened. Stretching and strengthening naturally go together. So the bonus is that as your body becomes more flexible, it is also getting stronger.

FLEXIBILITY

Stretching is also very important for sedentary individuals who are just getting into an exercise program. If you have been sedentary, it is likely that your muscles have adapted by becoming shorter and smaller and by losing their tone. This condition is known as disuse atrophy. Here too, stretching begins the process of lengthening your muscles, tendons and ligaments, restoring joint mobility, and restoring muscle strength. To help you in this we have included a gentle stretching routine for overall fitness at the end of this chapter.

Stretching becomes more important as one's level of exercise and fitness increases. Elite athletes often engage in only perfunctory stretching or, even worse, in ballistic stretching, which involves sudden and forceful movements which can easily result in an overstretching injury. In teaching stretching to Olympic and elite collegiate rowers, we found that they developed a new respect for stretching after taking a few classes which combined stretching with breathing and meditation techniques. They were also quite surprised at how strenuous it could be! These athletes have among the highest maxVO$_2$ and anaerobic thresholds of all athletes. They also have powerful bodies as a result of extensive weight training, running up and down thousands of steps in a stadium and, of course, rowing itself. Yet the majority wound up huffing and puffing from the stretching routine we were doing and learned firsthand that flexibility is as much a building block of total fitness as are aerobic conditioning and strength training.

So you can see that stretching has high value for individuals at every level of physical fitness, including the elite athlete, the recreational athlete, the sedentary individual and those with medical problems who want to move toward greater health.

What You Need to Know to Get Started

Your attitude and state of mind are extremely important in developing all aspects of fitness and human performance. This means that the quality of your attention is a key ingredient in the process of stretching. This is true whether you are doing your stretching routine as a warm-up or cool-down, or at a different time from your exercise program. This chapter will teach you how to develop concentration and a systematic awareness of what you are doing. The first step while you are stretching is to do it with complete attention! Experiment with treating the stretching routine you choose as an important and interesting entity in itself, to be experienced fully and not just to be gotten through because it's "good for you." We suggest that you keep it from becoming mechanical by noticing the minute details of how your body is feeling from one moment to the next and by keeping your attention tied to your breathing. Even if you have done these stretches a hundred or a thousand times in the past, each time you do the routine try to see it as new and fresh, as unique, which in fact it is. We call this attitude "beginner's mind." This is a term coined by the Zen Master Shunryu Suzuki who said: "In the beginner's mind there are many possibilities, in the expert's there are few."

If you follow the recommendations for stretching in this chapter, you will probably find out for yourself why yoga has become so popular recently among Americans and why stretching is really a fitness discipline in itself and a lot deeper than it may appear at first glance.

How Flexible Am I?

You are probably least flexible when you get out of bed and most flexible in the late afternoon or evening. Your body lengthens during the day and shortens while you sleep. You can test this for yourself very easily. Try to touch your toes as soon as you get out of bed. Measure where your fingers can reach with your knees straight; use a ruler if they don't touch the floor. Then retest yourself at various times of the day.

Not only does your body change in flexibility over the day but you may also have asymmetries. For example, your right hip may be more flexible than your left. As you do the stretching exercises, notice how one side of your body compares with the other.

In chapter 1 you will find some simple tests to give you a sense of how flexible you are now. Retest yourself from time to time to check your progress as you continue to practice stretching on a regular basis.

First Principles

1. Make the time to stretch. This can be the time of your warm-up before exercising or it can be at a totally separate time that you devote to developing increased flexibility.

2. Practice stretching regularly, *at least* 3 times a week for at least 15 minutes at a time.

3. If at all possible, stretch with your shoes off and in loose-fitting clothing.

4. It is best to stretch on an empty stomach.

5. Train yourself to breathe diaphragmatically for the entire time you devote to stretching. To practice diaphragmatic (also called abdominal or belly) breathing, lie on your back and place one hand on your belly. As you breathe in, see if you can *feel* your hand rise a little as your belly expands. As you breathe out, see if you can *feel* your hand go back toward the spine as your belly recedes. If your belly is relaxed, you will have no trouble perceiving this movement of your abdomen with your hand. Then take your hand away and feel the gentle expanding and receding of your belly, expanding as you breathe in, receding as you breathe out. It's as if there were a little balloon in your belly. The balloons (your lungs) are in your chest, of course, and not in your belly. But when you relax your belly, the diaphragm can descend further into your abdomen as you breathe in because there is less resistance from compressed organs, which adjust to the descent of the diaphragm by moving out a little. Babies breathe this way all the time; even from far away you can usually see a baby's belly rising and falling.

The diaphragmatic breath should be gentle and not forced. The belly will rise naturally on the inbreath and fall on the outbreath and should not be forcefully pushed out or pulled in. Once you get the hang of it, just practice "putting your mind in your belly" and riding the gentle waves of your own breathing at your belly. And each time you breathe out, allow yourself to sink a little deeper into the floor (or whatever surface you are lying on) as you send the conscious message to your muscles to "let go," soften and relax.

Once you become familiar with breathing in this way, you can do it all the time and particularly when you are doing your stretching. In the stretching routines in chapter 2, each stretch is accompanied by a recommended minimal number of breaths (inbreath plus outbreath) for which you should hold the position.

6. Let gravity be your friend and help you to relax into stretches.

7. Work at and within your body's limits with the intention of observing and exploring the boundary between what your body can do and where it says "stop." Never stretch beyond this limit to the point of pain.

Some discomfort is inevitable, and you need to learn how to enter this "stretching zone" where you are nourishing your body by exploring your limits but not damaging it. Damage—called "overstretching"—is possible if you are not being sensitive and attentive to what you are doing.

8. Repeat: Do not push *past* your limit! Stay *at the limit* and breathe.

9. As you breathe in, imagine that you can consciously direct your breath to any part of your body. It helps if you "direct" the inbreath to the regions of highest intensity in a particular stretch and imagine that you are breathing out from those regions as well. Practice directing your breath and your attention simultaneously to the regions of greatest intensity during the stretch. You can also imagine that the tension and fatigue are leaving your body with each outbreath and are being replaced on the inbreath with a sense of relaxation and vitality.

10. Stay at the boundary of a particular stretch long enough for your muscles to let go and actually relax into it. In the beginning of the stretch, you may find that you are unconsciously bracing yourself in many areas without needing to. After a while your body will realize this in some way. At this point you will find yourself letting go and "sinking" into the stretch.

11. When moving into a stretching position, breathe out as you move if it involves constricting your chest or belly region. If it involves expanding the chest or belly, breathe in as you make the movement.

12. Once a stretching position has been attained, breathe normally and diaphragmatically (see principle 5).

13. Keep your attention focused on the flow of your breathing and on the actual sensations you are experiencing as you do the stretching exercises and as you rest in between stretches. We recommend that for the first few weeks you count your breaths while you hold each stretch. This will help you maintain your focus in the present and will keep you in the stretches for an adequate amount of time. Remember to breathe slowly and deeply, without rushing the count.

14. Close your eyes from time to time to deepen your concentration and the focus on your body and your breathing.

15. When you notice your mind wandering off, or if you lose track of the count, you can choose to let your mind continue to wander. This can be pleasant and relaxing. But you can also work at developing greater concentration and achieve deeper states of relaxation and stillness by bringing your attention back to your body and your breathing whenever you notice that your attention has wandered off. This exercise introduces a powerful meditative approach for handling thoughts and distractions (see chapter 5), which can deepen your experience and the benefit you receive from the stretching routine.

16. Remember that all parts of your body are connected and con-

stitute a whole. If you are particularly interested in or concerned with one region of your body because you use it a lot (your legs, for example, if you are a runner) or because it is presenting problems for you, by all means direct a little more care and attention to that region. But also keep in mind that if you pay attention to your body as a whole from time to time, you will be indirectly promoting a higher degree of fitness for the parts of your body that concern you while you are also developing total body fitness.

17. The order in which you do the stretches is not that important. However, you should always begin with the gentle stretches that are relatively easy for you and then proceed toward more demanding ones as you become looser and more relaxed. Our stretching routines in the action plans are set up that way. You should feel free to modify the sequence if you find that you prefer a different order or would like to include other stretches or exclude some. Eventually you need to make the routine your own.

18. Remember to do your stretching with complete awareness. Do the exercises slowly and mindfully, keeping your attention in the present and tied to your breathing. Remember to cultivate your beginner's mind as you do them. Have fun!

STRETCHES FOR
PARTICULAR REGIONS OF YOUR BODY

Figs. 23–28 illustrate exercises for stretching particular regions of your body. If you wish to make up your own routine, we suggest that you try some from each group and change the combination from time to time for variety. You also can incorporate any of the stretches you like from among the specific routines in the action plans. The order is not particularly important, but you should do the easier ones first and compensate for stretches in one direction by doing stretches in the opposite direction as well.

FIG. 23.   Stretches for the back

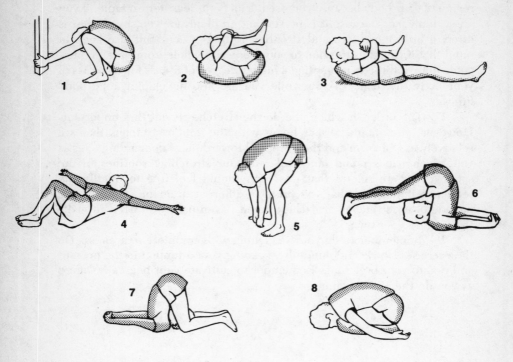

FIG. 24.   Stretches for the back of the legs

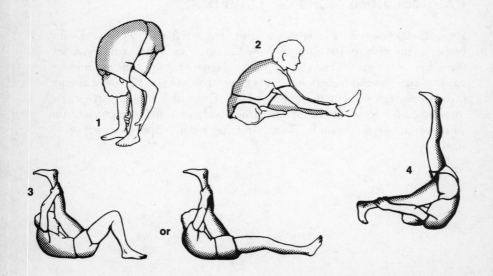

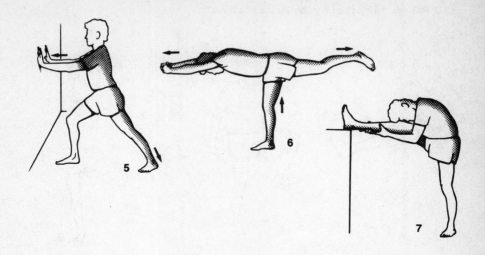

FIG. 25.   Stretches for the front of the legs and the hips

FIG. 26.   Stretches for the feet and ankles

FIG. 27.   Stretches for the neck

FIG. 28. Stretches for the arms and shoulders

GENTLE STRETCHING ROUTINE
FOR OVERALL FITNESS AND CONDITIONING

Fig. 29 shows a 12-part exercise known as sun salutations in yoga. It is to be done as a flowing movement, breathing in and out as indicated as you move into each position. In the beginning, you may want to forget about the flow and just assume each pose as best you can and hold it for a few breaths before attempting the next one. As it becomes more familiar, the flow will come naturally. This is a very popular exercise and is a good first step toward greater flexibility and fitness for those who have been leading a sedentary lifestyle.

We hope that this chapter and the specific stretching routines in chapter 2 will help you experience the benefits of increased flexibility and thereby support the other building blocks of your fitness program.

FIG. 29

1 Breathe in and out.

2 Breathe in.

3 Breathe out.

4 Breathe in.

6 Breathe out.

5 Hold the breath.

7 Breathe in.

8 Breathe out.

9 Breathe in.

10 Breathe out.

11 Breathe in.

12 Breathe in and out.

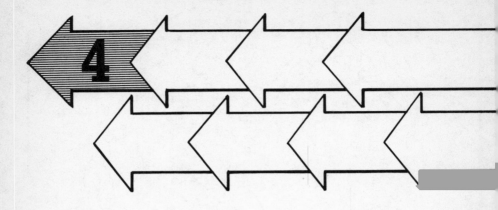

Whether you are a person active in sports or a competitive athlete, your sports performance level increases with strength training. In college football the saying is "with strength comes speed." Increased speed improves sports performance. More muscle power allows you to hit the ball harder or your opponent with more force. Better muscular endurance is of great benefit in all sports. So often games and matches are won or lost at the very end. Vince Lombardi reminded his players that "fatigue makes cowards of us all." Strength training helps defeat fatigue.

Many scientific studies have accurately documented that strength training reduces the risk of injury in sports. A study done in the New York State Public High School Athletic Association showed that the chance of suffering knee ligament injury is seventeen times greater when athletes compete in football with incompletely rehabilitated or weakened leg muscles. Strong athletes sustain fewer injuries.

It has always been accepted in medical circles that all humans lost strength as they aged. The older you were, the weaker you were. Recent scientific evidence shows that to be wrong. A study published in February 1985 in *The Journal of Orthopedic and Sports Physical Therapy* by Dr. Gail Drummer, Paul Vaccaro, and David Clarke from the University of Maryland argues against this theory. They showed that two female masters swimmers, ages 70 and 71, had greater muscle strength than less active women of the same age and were well within the normal range for normal women who were much younger. Their findings suggest that regular physical training will delay any decline in strength thought to be due to age.

STRENGTH

TRAINING

INCREASING MUSCLE STRENGTH

Muscles get stronger by being challenged. So too do the humans who own them. Muscles are adaptable biologic material. The harder they work, the stronger they become. Before strength training techniques were available, athletes did manual labor to increase their strength. Legendary football star Red Grange carried blocks of ice during the off season to develop strong legs.

This process of muscle strengthening is called the *stress adaptation principle*. When a muscle is stressed beyond its normal demands, it responds by becoming stronger. Once the muscle has adapted to the new stress, you can continue to strengthen it by challenging it with heavier weights. If the increase is too great the muscle will be damaged by the challenge and lose strength for a period of time. Hence, strength training must be slowly progressive. Don't be in a rush.

Prior to puberty or adolescence (below age 12 for girls and age 14 for boys), significant strength gains are not possible. It's not that it's dangerous to strength train at a younger age, it's just that it doesn't produce dramatic results.

You must have adult levels of sex hormones circulating in your bloodstream to get stronger. These hormones are androgens and testosterone. Androgens are manufactured in the adrenal glands of males and females. Testosterone is produced in the testicles of males. In general, males have bigger, stronger muscles than do females because they have testosterone in addition to androgens.

Androgens and testosterone are also called *anabolic steroids*. (The word *anabolic* refers to the constructive aspect of metabolism.) These are the steroids that some powerlifters, shot-putters and collision sports athletes have abused. Although they may produce strength gains, anabolic steroids also have serious medical side effects, and we strongly oppose using them (see chapter 8).

Muscles increase in size as they gain strength, as each muscle cell and fiber increases in size.

It is possible to violate the *stress adaptation principle* by overloading the muscle. This can result from lifting too much weight during one session or from allowing insufficient time between workouts. A muscle needs 48 hours between high-intensity strength training sessions to restore itself. This is called the *rebuilding time*. Ideally, the adaptation the muscle makes during this time leaves it somewhat stronger than when it was last challenged. If it is rechallenged before it has fully repaired itself, damage may result. The damage is usually at a microscopic level. Tiny rips or tears occur in the muscle substance that can only be seen through a microscope.

In view of this, a sensible workout schedule would be Monday–Wednesday–Friday or Tuesday–Thursday–Saturday. You can strength train every day, but work your upper and lower body on alternate days. If you miss one or several workouts, drop back two or three workouts so that you don't hurt yourself. Executed in this fashion, you can expect overall strength gains of 4% per week and 15% per month.

Always remember—*any strength training is better than none at all*.

GOALS

In order to set our goals and expectations intelligently, we must understand certain concepts about human muscle function. Sports performance involves movement. Your muscles are responsible for those movements. Tests have been invented to allow us to quantify sports performance according to the following:

- Strength
- Speed
- Power
- Endurance
- Maximum potential

Strength. This refers to the ability of muscles to apply or to resist force. The athlete who can bench press 300 pounds has twice the strength of one who can bench press 150 pounds. Strength is measured by performance in strength training exercises. In addition, a grip-strength hand-squeeze device is used to quantify arm and hand strength.

Speed. Speed relates to how quickly you can move your body over a certain distance. An individual who runs the 100-yard dash in 10 seconds has more speed than the individual who takes 13 seconds to cover the same distance. Increased strength leads to increased speed. Bruce Jenner proved this with a strength training program for the 1976 Olympics.

Power. Power is a combination of strength and speed. Suppose that two boxers have identical strength as measured by the amount of weight each can lift. However, one has the ability to deliver his punch with greater speed or velocity. This fast puncher has more power with which to knock out his opponent. Power is more critically important than sheer strength in most sports. Power can be measured by the vertical jump, the standing long jump or a softball throw, or on an isokinetic muscle testing machine.

Endurance. Endurance refers to the number of times that muscles can contract without fatigue and/or failure. This aspect of muscle function is obviously a key to performance in endurance sports or events such as the marathon.

Maximum potential. A comprehensive strength training program will allow you to maximize the potential of your skeletal muscles. In turn, this will help maximize your athletic potential. We all have upper limits to our potential. Here are some of the factors that determine those limits:

body type	age
bone length	sex
reaction time	attitude
coordination	environment

Body type. The shape of your body is inherited from your parents. In medicine, we call your body type your somatotype. The world is divided into three somatotypes: esthenic, or thin; mesomorphic, or muscular; ectomorphic, or heavy. If you are a mesomorph, you will be able to build more strength than the other two types. It's in your genes.

Bone length. Similarly, your bone length is an inherited characteristic. Scandinavians have long bones and Pygmies have short bones. Long bones are like long crowbars—they exert more force and leverage. The better the leverage the greater the strength potential.

Reaction time and *Coordination.* These are, in part, inherited traits. Carl Yastrzemski's father and son are both excellent hitters with exceptional hand-eye coordination. Sports competition and diligent practice can improve these skills.

Age. The best time in your life to build strength is from adolescence to age 30. These are the peak years in an athlete's life. However, ongoing strength training seems to maintain strength for many years. Scientific studies have shown that you don't have to lose strength as you get older— just keep strength training.

Sex. Samples of skeletal muscle from men and women look identical under a microscope. Prior to adolescence girls and boys have the same strength. Male hormone makes it possible for men to have bigger muscles than women. But if a man and a woman have the same body weight and muscle mass, they could have the same strength.

Attitude. Strength training requires some dedication, diligence and discipline. If you train on a regular basis, you will notice improvement in strength almost immediately. This leads to a positive attitude. You should look at it as an integral part of your lifetime fitness program.

Environment. Some people are limited by economic or geographical circumstances with respect to the availability of strength training equipment. Boys Clubs, YMCAs, schools and scholarships are all designed to bring equal opportunity to every young athlete.

WHY STRENGTH TRAIN?

Why should you bother to make the muscles of your body stronger? Among the reasons are

> appearance and confidence
> improved performance
> resistance to injury
> stopping the strength loss of aging

Your appearance improves because your muscles have "better tone." You are more firm and will look younger. Your muscles have better shape and contour. Your posture will improve and your stomach will be flatter. You will have more confidence in yourself.

STRENGTH TRAINING SYSTEMS

In sports today, there are three ways to challenge your muscles and strength train:

> Isometric training
> Isotonic training
> Isokinetic training

In Greek, the word *iso* means "equal." Therefore, *isometric* refers to equal lengths, *isotonic* refers to equal tension, and *isokinetic* refers to equal speed of motion.

Isometric training. The resistance against the muscle is constant and is of sufficient magnitude to prevent any shortening of the muscle or motion of the neighboring joints. An example: Push your hand against your forehead. Push so hard that your head can't move forward. That's an isometric contraction of the neck muscles. The pushing force against your forehead is too great for the neck muscles to overcome.

Isotonic training. The weight is constant but is light enough so that the muscle can shorten and the neighboring joints can move. Because your bones act as levers, the resistance against the muscle will not be constant throughout the whole exercise. Where the leverage is poor the muscle will work very hard. Where the leverage is favorable the muscle can loaf.

To defeat this variable leverage effect, the variable-resistance concept was invented. For instance, Nautilus machines use an "eccentric cam" device to push harder on the muscle as it gets more of a mechanical advantage because of leverage. Other machines use friction, fluids, levers or pulleys to achieve the same effect. By varying the resistance on the muscle, you force the muscle to work equally hard in every part of the exercise. This means that you can get muscles stronger over a period of time.

Variable-resistance isotonic machines were the first used for *negative-work* strength training. With this type of training, strengthening is achieved during the shortening (concentric) contraction as well as the lengthening (eccentric) contraction.

Isokinetic training. The muscle is forced to contract at a fixed rate of speed. For the speed to be fixed, the resistance must vary. It is a variable-resistance system with fixed speed so the muscle is maximally loaded at every point of muscle contraction and in the range of joint motion. The muscle is thus forced to do more work in the same period of time than is possible in the isometric or isotonic systems. Some isokinetic systems offer the ability to do concentric and eccentric strengthening. Studies have shown that high-speed isokinetic strength training may be more effective than any other method currently used.

Strength training systems include:

I. Isometric training
    Push against fixed objects
    Isometric bars
II. Isotonic training
    Fixed resistance
        free weights—many manufacturers
        Olympic weights
        Universal Gym (Nissen-Universal)
    Variable resistance
        Nautilus (Nautilus Sports/Medical Industries)
        Eagle (Cybex, division of Lumex)
        Mini-Gym
        Hydra-Fitness (Hydra-Gym)
III. Isokinetic training
    Cybex (division of Lumex)
    Kin-Com (Chattanooga Corporation)
    Lido (Loredan Biomedical)

STRENGTH TRAINING SYSTEMS

	Brand	Availability/Cost	Safety	
Isometric	Charles Atlas Dynamic Tension	No equipment needed Limited space needed Can be done anywhere	Excellent except for blood pressure increase	
Isotonic Fixed resistance	Free weights Universal Gym	Readily available Cheap	Good	
Variable resistance	Nautilus Eagle Mini-Gym Hydra-Fitness	Many commercial centers Somewhat expensive	Excellent	
Isokinetic	Cybex (Orthotron) Kin-Com Lido	Not readily available Quite expensive Requires professional supervision	Excellent	

STRENGTH TRAINING SAFETY

Safety in strength training is of prime importance for us all. There is risk in everything that we do. In strength training, the rewards more than outweigh the risks.

Strength (1–10 scale)	Power (1–10 scale)	Endurance (1–10 scale)	Disadvantages	Distinct Advantages
6	6	2	Blood pressure increase Strength gains specific to muscle length at exercise	Strengthening neck muscles Initial strength gains in muscles around joint injury or surgery (i.e., "quad sets")
8	8	8		Must control bar—aids muscle control in sports Variety of exercises
9	9	9		Contraction of muscle through full range of motion of joints Works eccentric and concentric phase of contraction
10	10	10		Fastest safe strength gains Kin-Com works eccentric and concentric contraction
	Especially high-speed isokinetic training			

In ten years of a sports medicine orthopedic practice, we have seen very few injuries resulting from strength training. Interestingly, the few injuries treated have been in experienced powerlifters. They lift such enormous amounts of weight that they can actually tear a muscle in half.

Other injuries tend to be minor. Pinched fingers, bruised toes and

roughened skin constitute most of them. The low back is the major excep-
tion. You are *never* too young and *never* too experienced to hurt your
back in strength training.

Learn proper technique so that your low back is always in a strong
mechanical position. Use a leather or elastic weightlifting belt for any
standing exercise involving more than 100 pounds. Be sure to do sit-ups
to keep your abdominal muscles strong. All health professionals agree
that strong belly muscles keep your low back healthy. Finally, be certain
to stretch out your back before each strength training session.

Here are some other good safety tips:

See your doctor for a physical if you are over 35 years old.

Warm up with stretching and jumping jacks for 5–10 minutes.

Wear comfortable shoes with rubber soles that won't slip.

Use a leather or elastic weightlifting belt, especially if you are
using heavy weights.

Have a partner work with you when you are using free weights,
especially when doing bench presses.

Learn good technique—proper stance and posture.

Set expectations intelligently—don't lift too much too soon.

Try to maintain your program on a regular basis—*don't* strength
train occasionally.

YOUR STRENGTH TRAINING PROGRAM

Here are the basic ingredients of any comprehensive strength training
program:

Specificity—which specific muscles to work

Intensity—how much weight or resistance you should lift

Duration—how many times you should do each exercise (we call this
how many reps or repetitions)

Frequency—how many workouts per week

Systems—which equipment you should use

Specificity. Since there are 434 skeletal muscles in the body, we
would ideally like to strengthen each one. When you engage in sports you
challenge virtually every one of those muscles. However, for the sake of
simplicity, we must work to build strength in the muscles of these areas of
your body.

Trunk muscles
  chest
  back
  abdominals
Limb muscles
  shoulders
  upper arms
  forearms
  thighs
  calves

As you can see, we are built like a tree with a trunk and limbs. The exercises presented here are designed to build generalized strength. Some exercises work several areas simultaneously; others work only one at a time. For example, a bench press challenges primarily the chest and shoulder muscles. However, it also works the triceps muscle on the back of your upper arm. In addition, your back and forearm muscles act as stabilizers of the bar. Conversely, wrist curls strengthen only the forearm muscles.

Here are the strength training exercises we use (see figs. 30–41):

Chest—bench presses
Back—bent-over rows
Abdominals—leg raises; sit-ups
Shoulders—military presses; upright rows
Upper arms—biceps curls; triceps extensions
Forearms—front wrist curls; reverse wrist curls
Thighs—quadriceps extensions; hamstring curls
Calves—toe raises with weights on shoulders

If you can master these exercises using free weights, you can easily convert to other systems.

Intensity. If you have never lifted weights or have not strength trained for two or more years, start with just the weight of the bar. If you are using weight machines, adjust to the lowest setting.

Duration. Try to do 10 repetitions of each exercise. When you use variable-resistance isotonic or isokinetic machines, your muscles will be exhausted with 10 reps. With free weights or the Universal Gym you can do a second set of 10 reps on each exercise. Once you can do the 10 reps with ease, increase the weight by 5–10 pounds.

Frequency. Allow 48 hours between strength training workouts. This gives muscles sufficient time to recover and strengthen.

Systems. There are three basic systems for strength training—isometric, isotonic and isokinetic. You should choose the system that is available, affordable and convenient.

FIG. 30.   Bench press

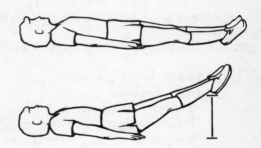

FIG. 31.   Bent-over row

FIG. 32.   Leg raise

FIG. 33.   Sit-up

FIG. 34.   Military press

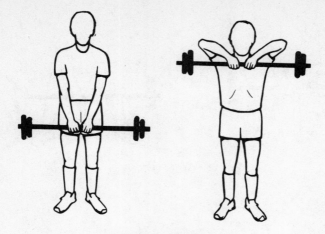

FIG. 35.   Upright row

FIG. 36.   Biceps curl

FIG. 37.   Triceps extension

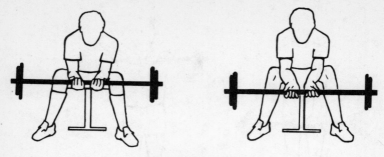

FIG. 38.   Wrist curl

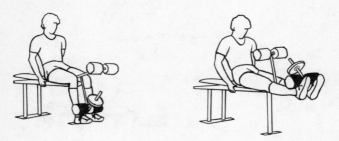

FIG. 39.   Quadriceps extension

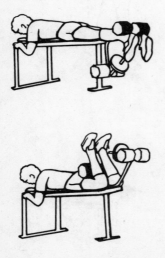

FIG. 41.   Toe raise with weights on shoulders

FIG. 40.   Hamstring curl

YOUR STRENGTH TRAINING CHECKLIST

Which system: Consider cost, safety, convenience.

Which exercises: work all basic muscle groups of the body.

How much weight: Start with the bar or the lowest weights on any machine.

How many reps: Do 10 reps on average, never more than 12. Do as many sit-ups and leg raises as possible.

How many sets: Do one set if using machines, two sets on free weights.

How many times per week: Train three times per week; allow 48 hours between strength training sessions.

How fast to advance: Take it slow; at most, add 10 pounds every three to four weeks. What's the rush? It should be a lifelong commitment.

What cadence to use for each rep: Push or pull the weight up into position on a 2 count (positive work). Let back into starting position on a 5 count (negative work). By doing positive and negative work, you will get strong faster with the same investment of time.

Which order of exercise: Start at the top of the list and work down. Feel free to vary the order to prevent boredom.

STRETCHING ROUTINE FOR WEIGHT TRAINING AND NAUTILUS

Both free-weight work and Nautilus work should be pursued in conjunction with a stretching program! Unfortunately, most people who pursue fitness training of this kind have little interest in stretching and tend to be preoccupied with strength, endurance and appearance. If true fitness is your goal, however, then increasing strength and endurance must be accompanied by adequate flexibility, since, as we point out in chapter 3, muscles which are repeatedly exercised against resistance shorten and become less flexible. Fig. 42 illustrates a sequence to stretch the ten major muscle groups and keep you limber. Do it before and after your weight or Nautilus workout according to the principles discussed in chapter 3. You will also get more overall benefit and pleasure from your strength/power work if you do it with the mental strategies discussed in chapter 5. In particular, perform each movement with awareness of your breathing, of the actual sensations in the muscles being worked, of your body's overall movement. Be sure to relax all muscles not actively engaged in the movement (e.g., the feet when doing leg curls).

Go through the entire sequence, holding each stretch for at least the number of breaths indicated and alternating sides when required. Remember to breathe slowly and deeply from your belly; feel free to rest between stretches for as long as you like. Consult chapter 3 for more information on the principles to keep in mind as you do this sequence. This 20-step routine should take you at least 12 minutes.

FIG. 42

1 breath.

3 breaths.

5 breaths.

5 breaths.

10 breaths.
Alternate sides.

10 breaths. Alternate sides.

10 breaths. Alternate sides.

8

10 breaths. Alternate sides.

9

10 breaths.

10

10 breaths.

11

10 breaths.

12

3 breaths.

13

3 breaths.

14

5 breaths.

15

10 breaths.

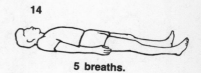

16

10 breaths.

17

10 breaths.

18

15 breaths.

19

10 breaths. Alternate sides.

20

10 breaths. Alternate sides.

MUSCLE STRENGTH, POWER AND ENDURANCE ACTION PLAN

Body Area	Exercise	Repetitions	Weight
Chest	Bench presses	10	Start with bar alone or lowest setting on machine
Back	Bent-over rows	10	
Abdominals	Leg raises Sit-ups	As many as possible	Do not use weights
Shoulders	Military presses Upright rows	10 10	Start with bar alone or lowest setting on machine
Upper arms	Biceps curls Triceps extensions	10 10	Advance 10 pounds when you can easily do 10 reps
Forearms	Front wrist curls Reverse wrist curls	10 10	

Thighs	Quadriceps-knee
	    extensions
	Hamstring-knee
	    curls
		10
		
		10
			Once at a comfortable weight level don't add 10 pounds again for 3–4 weeks

Calves	Toe raises with
	    weights on
	    shoulders
		10	Start with bar alone or lowest setting on machine

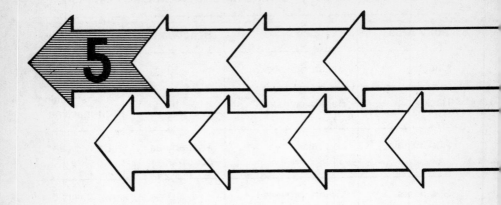

Mental factors play an enormous role in determining how we perform, whether in competitive sports, recreational sports, at work or school, or in our personal lives. How many times have you been in a situation in which you momentarily lost your self-confidence and performed poorly at something you should have done well and easily? And how often have you avoided or postponed doing something that you knew was important for you to do and that deep down you really wanted to do because you lacked the mental energy, the motivation to get yourself to do it, and in the process subverted your own best intentions? Lack of motivation, self-doubt, fear, poor concentration, trying too hard, self-consciousness, frustration, anger, boredom, a busy mind which won't shut down—these are just a few of the mental obstacles that sometimes prevent us from doing our best and from deriving satisfaction from what we do. If such psychological factors predominate when we attempt to perform or accomplish something, we can easily become discouraged and more unsure of ourselves, and this, of course, makes matters even worse.

Once we come to recognize that, at least sometimes, our own thought patterns and emotions can undermine our capacity to do our best, we may be drawn naturally to consider how we might go about learning to improve our mental functioning to optimize our capacity to perform. How do we go about achieving a degree of control over our own minds? In the domain of performance, it becomes extremely important to control those mental reactions that undermine our ability to perform at our best, and to develop new attitudes and strategies to focus the mind and make maximum use of its powers of intentionality, concentration and relaxation. The purpose of this chapter is to give you some background for understanding the role of the mind in performance and to help you get

MENTAL

STRATEGIES

started on a systematic program to develop your own greater control in the areas that matter most to you.

Mental preparation now plays an important role in the training of elite athletes. Gymnasts, rowers, tennis players, cyclists, swimmers, runners, jumpers, archers, shooters, divers, weightlifters, skiers, and basketball, baseball, football, soccer and hockey players all use mental strategies to relax, enhance concentration, build emotional stability and resilience, as well as to correct technique. Some teams do this very systematically; others don't, leaving it for the individual athletes to find their own way to mental training if they are so inclined.

Effective methods of mental training are now increasingly in demand, not only among elite athletes, but also among recreational athletes. And in fact, mental strategies for stress reduction and relaxation are now being adopted by people everywhere and are used in a wide range of situations by chief executives, secretaries, police, doctors, trial lawyers, and hospital patients. All are motivated by the realization that the mind holds untapped potential to help us to work and to heal and to live our lives more fully.

Progress in this building block of sports performance can be most effectively accomplished if we are willing to become more familiar with what our mind is actually doing from moment to moment, and if we are open to learning new ways to channel our mental energies. The first step is deceptively simple but crucial: Start paying attention to what you are actually doing and feeling. Become more familiar with your mind's fluctuations and its internal dialogue.

Why is awareness of our mental activity such a fundamental factor in performance? In a word, because we become so easily absorbed, without even knowing it, in the elaborate constructs of our own minds, in particular, in our thoughts and feelings. When this occurs, it is often at the expense of other important dimensions of our being which are essential for optimal functioning. Instead of remaining open to and trusting the direct perception of our senses, for instance, we function to a large extent in a world which is the creation of our own thoughts. Because our thought content is often self-critical, judgmental, opinionated and inaccurate, it tends to distort our views and perceptions and therefore what we do and how we do it. Moreover, such thoughts in particular can trigger strong emotional reactions that can be troublesome, inappropriate and self-defeating. Simply by restoring context and perspective, awareness can correct and reduce the negative effects your thinking can have on performance when it becomes judgmental or critical or fearful. The development and application of this capacity lead to greater mental stability and "centeredness," as well as the ability to restore mental equilibrium quickly when it is lost.

Tim Gallwey, author of *The Inner Game of Tennis* and other books about inner aspects of performance, once remarked, quoting the psychologist Fritz Perls, that the human species has the unique distinction of being the only species on the planet that is capable of interfering with its own growth. Gallwey argues convincingly that this is mainly because our cerebral, thinking self dominates too much at the wrong times and in the wrong ways, causing us to lose touch with our deeper self, which is usually quite competent and which needs a different approach to training to express itself optimally.

The body has a wisdom of its own. Not only can it perform extremely coordinated movements such as walking, running and catching, but it can learn to do them without thinking and without being told how. Yet this wisdom of the body often remains unfelt or underutilized because our thinking overrides it with strong ideas about the way things *should be,* what the body should be doing and how. It sometimes seems as if the aspect of us that thinks does not trust the part of us that executes. Yet it is the body that ultimately executes whatever needs to be done in terms of movement, coordination and timing. And it can do this optimally, especially in sports, only if there is a basic trust in this wisdom of the body. So one really needs to support this quality through awareness of it and know, again through awareness, when to give messages to the body, what kind of messages to give and when to just let go and be still.

The best and most satisfactory performances occur when the artificial distinction between "mind" and "body" dissolves altogether and a person functions as a unified whole. When this happens there is no tension between thinking or feeling and doing, and thus no working against oneself. This is not such an extraordinary state. Children, for instance, are far less fragmented in this regard than adults. They feel and act as whole beings because they have not yet developed the refined discriminating thought processes that tend to veil adults from the world of the senses and feeling. As adults, we usually have to *learn* how to use our thought processes without letting them wall us off from the rest of our experience.

For most adults, functioning as a whole organism is something we need to work at, to practice. According to Roger Walsh, M.D., a prominent psychiatrist and student of the interface between Eastern and Western psychologies, all traditional Eastern psychologies view our usual mode of mental functioning as extremely suboptimal. In the Eastern experience, rigorous mental training in a meditation discipline is seen as essential in order to free oneself from the distortions in thinking and emotional reactivity which undermine the expression of our intrinsic wholeness. Gallwey's work pioneered the application of methods originating in the meditative traditions to the domain of sports performance. As we pointed out earlier, the first step in the process of developing greater mental control is to commit yourself to the discipline of paying attention to your own inner as well as outer experience. Self-observation and self-inquiry are really the foundation of all meditation practices and where you need to begin. This kind of paying attention does not involve efforts to change yourself as much as simply a willingness to see yourself as you really are. It involves learning to listen and to trust the wisdom of your body and of your being. It means learning to see your own thoughts with detached awareness. It means being aware of your inner dialogue and of the ways that dialogue colors and distorts your view of the world. To cultivate this listening, this commitment to paying attention, you will need to develop the ability to enter states of relaxed concentration and detach the content of your thinking.

This is best done by practicing, on a regular basis, the exercises described in this chapter. Devoting a little time and energy to these new strategies for learning about yourself can be profoundly useful on many levels and, of course, applies to all aspects of human functioning, not just sports and exercise. One benefit is that your trust in yourself will grow and you will be able to face and navigate through stressful situations in your life with greater clarity and control. No approach holds *the* answer to all life's problems. We are only suggesting that you have a far greater capacity to face and handle all aspects of your life than you probably realize and that these exercises can be of considerable help along the way.

Coaches and sport psychologists employ a number of different methods of mental training to enhance performance in athletes. Among these are self-hypnosis, progressive relaxation, meditation, biofeedback, autogenic training and mental rehearsal. In many ways these techniques are all different ways of accomplishing the same thing. At this point, there has not been enough scientific research to decide their relative merits, but it is probable that they will all be found to have value and that different athletes will be drawn to different approaches depending on their personalities and their specific sports.

What these methods have in common is that they are alternatives to our ordinary way of taking control. The Swedish sport psychologist, Dr. Lars-Eric Uneståhl emphasizes that we usually seek control by exercising "conscious will and determination: we *do* things, we *achieve* results, we *exert* ourselves, we *work* hard." We know how things should be, what to expect, and we *try, try, try* to make them be that way. Dr. Uneståhl, who has tested his methods of inner mental training on over 5,000 Swedish athletes, including numerous national and Olympic teams, points out that although conscious will and determined effort are very important factors in training athletes, in many situations *they do not work at all*. Thus, willpower cannot be the sole basis for an effective mental strategy for improving performance.

As a simple example, take *trying* to relax or *trying* to fall asleep. The harder you try, the more determined the effort, the less likely it is that you will achieve the desired result. This is an example of well-intentioned self-interference. There is a basic schism between your thoughts and feelings about what needs accomplishing, and "the rest of you," which ultimately "does" the accomplishing. This schism can lead to great frustration, anger and loss of confidence. And the more you try to assert control through determined efforts of the will, the larger the problem becomes. In such a case, what is required is *an alternative method of control* that will allow you to "let go" into relaxation or sleep. Paradoxically, sometimes the only way you can achieve control in certain situations is to give up trying to achieve control, at least in the usual way.

Most mental obstacles to performance are of this nature. They are not *solved* by conscious effort or exertion of the will, but can readily *dissolve* if one adopts a different approach. So if you can get to sleep easily, you are already a master of letting go into unconsciousness! But if you want to perform optimally when you are awake, the question is, can you learn to let go into a relaxed state of *heightened* consciousness?

Let's take a look at what happens at times when we are not interfering with our own functioning. Sometimes this just happens spontaneously. Have you ever had an experience of doing anything at all in which the doing just flowed out of you while you remained completely relaxed and your mind was calm and aware? Abraham Maslow, the founder of humanistic psychology, called these moments "peak experiences." Uneståhl interviewed a number of top gymnasts after peak performances to see how they described their inner experiences during those times. He concluded that they were in what he calls an ideal performing state (IPS), which he sees as a nonordinary or "altered" state of consciousness. Peak experiences are usually characterized by a sense of non-doing, of witnessing. They are usually associated with an intense absorption of attention so that even if there is an awareness of the external surroundings, this can in no way detract from one's performance or experience. It is as if whatever is happening is just unfolding on its own, and you would be truly and genuinely reluctant to take credit for it as if *you* were actually responsible for its happening. It is difficult to find adequate words for such an experience. Athletes describe their experiences at such moments as feelings of acute well-being, peace, calm, stillness, detachment, freedom, unity, being in the present, instinctive action and surrender.

The "runner's high" is an experience of this kind. When you "hit your stride," it can seem perfectly effortless to run, sometimes for great distances and at unusual speed. And it feels as if the running is just happening, that there is no "you" doing it. This is because the mind has come into a nonordinary state of consciousness, a state characterized by relaxed concentration and a detached awareness. Thoughts, fears and doubts can no longer undermine your performance because in this state of mind they either do not arise or no longer have their ordinary power to absorb your attention. It's as if your mind has gone beyond thinking to a realm of moment-to-moment awareness in which the entity we usually refer to as "I" seems like just another thought rather than the ultimate source of your decisions and actions.

Athletes in all sports have described experiences of this kind at moments of peak performance. These experiences cannot be made to happen by efforts of will, but they occur more commonly in athletes who practice some form of systematic psychological training. This is because the methods themselves evoke, deepen and facilitate access to the factors that appear to form the foundation of the ideal performing state—namely, concentration, relaxation, letting go of thoughts and effort, and feelings of harmony and flow. Meditation makes use of awareness, concentration and relaxation practices and sometimes visualization to develop these qualities. Hypnosis uses relaxation, trance and suggestion, often in the form of imaging and mental rehearsal. Biofeedback applies a combination of these in conjunction with machines to amplify relevant aspects of body functioning such as brain waves, heartbeat or muscle firing. These approaches to mental control all emphasize some form of relaxation, letting go and allowing things to happen rather than trying to make things happen. They also differ in important ways that may influence what you are drawn to doing yourself, depending on your personality, the sport you are involved in and your goals.

Meditation is the most general and fundamental of these methods. We will introduce you to the basic meditative approach to optimizing functioning. From our work with collegiate and Olympic rowers, we have come to feel that this approach provides the most fundamental and reliable foundation for mental training. Within this global strategy, specialized variations and refinements involving hypnotic suggestion, cognitive restructuring, imaging and mental rehearsal can be totally appropriate. However, without foundation in meditative awareness, the other techniques can often lead to problems such as becoming too goal-oriented. In fact, without this foundation, the other techniques can easily become a new way of getting caught up in trying too hard or in wishful thinking, resulting in a return to the old and generally ineffective ways of trying to control performance.

The reason that meditation is a fundamental and global strategy is that it has to do with awareness and attention. You cannot function optimally in any domain without knowing what needs attending to and what does not and how to regulate your attention. By practicing paying attention, you develop a capacity to enter states of deep concentration and physiological relaxation. Practicing intentionally paying attention, both formally while remaining still and informally, during exercise and daily activities, leads to an enhanced sensitivity and awareness of your body, your thoughts and feelings, as well as of external stimuli and events. It also leads to a capacity to function from within states of heightened awareness once they become familiar to you. In identifying your thoughts as they come up as "events in the field of your consciousness" rather than necessarily accurate representations of an objective reality, you are far less likely to get caught up in them and succumb to their interference with your capacity to act appropriately. So, far from being magical or mystical, meditation is actually quite down-to-earth and practical. Perhaps the following two examples of what we are calling meditative strategies will give you a better sense of how they may be applied in real-life situations.

Seat racing

Rowing has a peculiar if not unique method for determining which athletes will actually row together as a team and get a chance to compete. This involves a process called seat racing, in which two boats will race repeatedly against each other. After each race, the coach will make one switch of two rowers at corresponding seat positions in the boats. The test is to see which boat goes faster when the rowers are switched, assuming all other things remain equal. This can be a very grueling experience psychologically as well as physically. For one thing, your performance can be the deciding factor in whether you make the team at all in a national team selection, or whether you make the varsity boat at the collegiate level. Since all rowers know that basically they will be in one-on-one competition with each other before they will ever be able to row together as a team, it makes for a great deal of tension during the selection process. Often close friends or roommates, or former members of a winning boat, are obliged to seat race against each other. Usually at least some of the other rowers in the boats who are not being seat raced at a particular time know the two who are being tested quite well and, of course, may be partial to one athlete or the other and have conflicting feelings. All of this tension defines the mental topology of seat racing. This kind of emotional conflict can totally undermine the rower's performance just when it is most important to produce a peak effort. Thus it is very important for a rower who is being seat raced to be able to clear his or her mind of all thoughts and feelings about *whom* he or she is racing against and about the meaning of winning or losing a particular race, and just row as well as possible. Rowers who practiced meditation techniques reported a far greater capacity to maintain emotional stability under the pressures of seat racing after they had learned to meditate. They also felt much better about both their own performances and about the final outcome of the selection process.

The marathon

A number of studies have compared the mental strategies of world-class marathoners to those of recreational marathoners. Since the marathon is such a grueling event, one might think that one strategy for enduring the pain and the monotony of the miles is to distract oneself, either by thinking about other places or by doing problems in one's head or by daydreaming, and so on. And indeed, in a number of studies, recreational marathoners as a rule used this strategy to cope with the pain and the distance. But not so the world-class runners! Their strategies involved monitoring exactly what they were experiencing, tuning into the actual sensations in their feet and legs. It is important to realize that both types of strategies work. Distraction and tuning out can help you endure a long race. But as a rule, they are not usually effective strategies for winning, or for optimizing performance. For that, awareness and tuning in are preferable, even though they may lead to greater awareness of pain and fear.

Everything that has been said up to this point has been directed to your analytical, thinking self, which is going to need reasons for deciding to incorporate systematic mental training exercises into your efforts to improve performance. This is an important decision, but once it is made, the real work begins. In the following sections we have outlined a number of these exercises. You need to actually *do* them and *practice* using them on a regular basis if you want them to help improve your performance. This does not take that much extra time, in part because it involves being aware of your experience, attitudes and behavior as you are living and functioning and performing. You can start by paying systematic attention to those aspects of your experience that you may have been ignoring up to now. But if you are serious about mental training, we strongly recommend that you make time to practice the concentration and relaxation exercises in a formal way for at least 20 minutes a day. Let this time be a time to just be, a time to let go of all doing and of your ideas. Just allow your being to express itself and observe its expression nonjudgmentally from moment to moment. Doing so will greatly improve your capacity to apply these relaxation and concentration skills in many different aspects of your life, including competitive and stressful situations.

STRATEGIES FOR MAINTAINING MOTIVATION

Millions of Americans have taken up regular exercise programs in the past fifteen years. The motivation for doing so varies but usually involves the desire for better health and fitness. But the factors motivating you to start an exercise program may not be those motivating you to continue with it. Most people continue to exercise because they feel better when they do, both physically and mentally. Exercise can become a positive addiction in the sense that once you experience how well you can feel, you are naturally drawn to continue developing this side of yourself. People report that regular exercise helps them relieve stress, concentrate better at work, release negative emotions and see things in greater perspective. We suggest that you periodically make a list of the factors that motivate you to do what you are doing. Also make a list of those factors that undermine your motivation or produce resistance in you. By doing so, you will develop a healthy awareness of the different forces at work within your own mind which influence your level of commitment to what you are doing. Here are two suggestions we have found helpful in developing and maintaining motivation:

1. Become comfortable with the idea of *self-responsibility*. Be willing to recognize that, to a large extent, how you live your life—how you allocate your time and energy, what you do and how you do it—is a matter of choice. Of course, it may not seem this way and you may feel that your life is totally caught up in schedules and responsibilities beyond your control. Look a little deeper and see whether this too is not a matter of choice. Is it possible that you have already chosen not to change, chosen to rationalize the status quo? Is there no room in your life for a fresh vision, for new possibilities, for new choices, for reorienting priorities, for growth? We have never met an individual in whom these possibilities did not exist, but we have met many who refused to recognize them. This itself is a choice, albeit perhaps an unconscious one.

2. Become comfortable with the concept that *self-discipline* is essential for realizing important objectives. Self-discipline means the intention to do what you have chosen to do even though at times parts of your mind will tell you that you don't need to do it "today." It is helpful to ponder your goals, prioritize them and then allocate your resources of time and energy in a doable way. Develop a realistic schedule for yourself, one that is neither so hard that you are bound to fail, nor so lacking in intensity

that no depth can come of it. Honor your intentions and actually do what you have chosen and prescribed for yourself. *You don't have to like it or dislike it, feel like it or not feel like it!* These feelings will come and go. Just do it because you *have* to do it, because you have already chosen to do it. If you have a lot of trouble with this concept, try visualizing yourself the way you want to be, as described in the section on imaging and mental rehearsal. Imagine yourself functioning with strong intentionality and less susceptibility to your own excuses. If you proceed in this way, you will very soon find a new strength growing within yourself, a new power of mind, the power of your individual intentionality. All serious athletes and performers have developed this level of commitment. Without it, there can be no realization of individual potential.

STRATEGIES FOR DEVELOPING CONCENTRATION

Concentration is steadiness of attention. If you observe your own mind, you will probably find that it jumps around all over the place, that it is not so easy to focus on one object or maintain attention on that object for any period of time. Our attention is easily caught up in our own thoughts, or in feelings, sensations, impulses, distracting sounds or other external occurrences. Yet attention is critical to performance. If your mind is preoccupied by anything that takes your attention away from what you need to be aware of, even for an instant, it can have a serious negative effect on your performance. This is particularly true in high-stress situations. In such situations, it is most important to have a clear and concentrated mind, undistracted and unfettered by thoughts or feelings that are irrelevant to the task to be accomplished, so that you can let yourself do what you have trained to be able to do, so that you can let yourself perform at your peak capacity. People commonly misunderstand this and think that meditation involves suppressing your thoughts and feelings. Actually this is not true at all. What is involved is learning to keep the mind one-pointed in the presence of a constant background flux of thoughts and feelings, which gradually and naturally subside as concentration deepens.

Concentration is a skill you can best develop by meditating every day. As we have said, there is nothing magical or mystical about meditation. It is simply paying attention *on purpose*. Try this simple exercise for 5 or 10 minutes:

1. Sit in a comfortable place where you will not be interrupted. Assume a dignified posture with your back, neck and head erect but not stiff and your shoulders relaxed. Keep your feet flat on the

floor if you are sitting in a chair. You may also sit cross-legged on the floor, but this is not necessary.

2. Allow your eyes to close or let them remain half-open with the gaze stable and unfocused.

3. Become aware of your breathing at your belly (see chapter 3 on diaphragmatic breathing).

4. Just observe (or feel) the inbreath and the outbreath for a few minutes.

5. Count each outbreath as you observe (feel) it, starting with 1 and going to 10. Then start the count over again at 1 with the next outbreath.

6. If you lose track of the count at any time, or go beyond 10, when you become aware of it simply note that you have had a lapse in concentration, and begin at 1 again on the next outbreath.

7. When 5 or 10 minutes are up, watch (feel) your breath without counting for a minute or so and then resume your activities.

What did you notice while doing this? Did you lose track of the count at all? What took your mind away? How quickly did it register that you were no longer watching (feeling) your breath and counting? Did you find yourself mechanically counting *in*breaths at a certain point without realizing what you were doing? All are common experiences when one first tries this kind of exercise. If you practice this exercise on a regular basis you will find your ability to steady and quiet the mind improving. Your concentration will deepen and become more reliable in circumstances when you actually need to be highly focused and concentrated. We recommend that you practice with the counting for four weeks and after that just sit regularly and watch your breathing without counting, keeping your attention focused on each inbreath and on each outbreath, as described in chapter 3. And every time your mind wanders off and you come to realize that it is no longer on the breath, just bring it back to your belly and to your breathing. And don't be hard on yourself because your mind wandered off! Everybody's mind does. Just bring it back as soon as you become aware of it. Concentration requires ongoing practice.

Once you have it down, you can use this simple meditative concentration exercise in many ways. To begin with, you can use it while you are exercising. Keep your attention on your breathing as you work out. The breathing is a very powerful focus for your attention, as you will see if you practice attending to it for any length of time. Pay attention to other rhythmic and repetitive aspects of your exercise program, such as the footfall or arm swing in walking or running, the feet pedaling on a bike, slide control or the catch in rowing, the feeling of the hands pulling on the water in swimming, and so on. Whatever you choose as the object of your focused attention, keep your attention on it and bring your mind back to it every time your mind wanders off. This concentration exercise can add a new dimension to any sport. For endurance sports such as running, biking and swimming, it can help you overcome boredom and handle fatigue and pain better, as well as increase your pleasure from exercising. You can also use awareness of your breathing in your daily life, at work and at home. It is a natural vehicle for centering yourself (see the following section on relaxation) and staying calm and focused in stressful situations. Further on you will find a series of awareness exercises you can use to reinforce this process.

STRATEGIES FOR RELAXATION

Relaxation is a complex and dynamic psychophysiologic condition. It is characterized by reduced skeletal muscle tension, lower heart rate and blood pressure, lower oxygen consumption, lower blood lactate levels, lower skin conductance and lower serum catecholamine levels. It is usually accompanied by feelings of well-being and equanimity. It is a state incompatible with anxiety and thus extremely useful to cultivate. Almost all the athletes with whom we have worked report that they are much more calm at the start of a race and much less likely to make mistakes due to anxiety and hyperarousal since they began to develop their capacity to relax under pressure.

Fortunately for you, you do not need to practice yet another technique to accomplish this. The meditation technique that you used in the concentration exercise also promotes relaxation. We suggest that you extend the meditation practice to 20 minutes a day if you want to have the relaxation carry over into the rest of your day. You should also know that this exercise doesn't always have to feel relaxing to be beneficial. In fact, sometimes when you sit in meditation it will be anything but relaxed. You may feel uptight and tense, worried and preoccupied. It may seem as though it is impossible to concentrate because of the storm of thoughts and feelings within you. It may even seem that the meditation was what produced the tension and the storm. Here is where your self-discipline can serve you well. These are some of the best times to practice being still in the meditation and just letting it all wash over you. You can stay with the awareness of your breathing or focus on the tension itself, or on your stormy thoughts, or on whatever predominates in the field of your awareness. This is not the same as thinking or daydreaming! What you are doing is "being with" thoughts, feelings, tension, experiencing them as they arise in each moment and letting them go without getting absorbed in their content. Or if at any point you become aware that your attention has lapsed, then in that moment, you just return to observing thoughts and feelings in the present as a flow of events in the field of your awareness. Again, this may not *feel* relaxing at all. But if you think of relaxation as a deep feeling of self-acceptance, as a state of being so comfortable in your own skin that you can accept the tension or discomfort or fear because that is not you but just a passing manifestation of your mind at the moment, then you will begin to see why this practice is in fact the heart of relaxation.

It may help to think of your mind as a deep lake. The surface may be calm if there is no wind, but it may also be rough in a storm. But ten feet down, the water is always still! If you can cultivate the capacity to find calmness and equanimity within your own being even when the surface is tense and anxious, you will be practicing true relaxation and you will probably notice that at least two things begin to happen. One, you will take yourself a little less seriously and see the humor in your own tension, and two, you will have better control over the tension so that you are less anxious in general. What you are doing is learning to accept and trust yourself, even when you don't like a particular aspect of your behavior.

Awareness Exercises

1. Ask yourself from time to time during your day: Am I awake and aware or am I on automatic pilot? Bring your attention to your breathing and just watch it for a few breaths.

2. While exercising, be aware of your breathing. Just let it flow naturally and watch it.

3. While exercising, or at any other time you remember to try it while your body is moving, bring your attention to your breathing and then let it expand until you are keenly aware of your body as a whole, from head to toe. Just be aware of your whole body moving, flowing. Allow yourself to let go into effortless movement.

4. Watch your thoughts while you exercise. Are they judgmental and critical? Are they about the past or about the future? See your thoughts as events in the field of your awareness and let them go. Dwell in present moment experience.

5. In stressful situations, observe yourself as your level of body tension increases. Bring awareness to your body. Where is the tension greatest? How does it feel? Let the tension flow out on the outbreath.

6. In stressful situations, observe your thoughts and feelings. Are you feeling insecure, defensive, worried about the future? Be aware of the content of your thoughts. Don't try to suppress your thoughts or make

them go away or even replace them with more positive thoughts. Just let each thought or feeling register, then let go of it and come back to your breathing, directing your attention to your belly, and feeling it move as you breathe. See what happens and make a note of it.

7. In stressful communications, ask yourself if you are really listening to the other person or persons. Then pay attention. Hear what the other person is really saying. Try to see this person as a whole being, as who he or she is and not who your thoughts are saying he or she is. Become aware of the roles you assume when communicating. Are these mechanical and unconscious, or intentional and conscious?

8. Be aware of the statements you make to yourself. Are they accurate? Can you let go of these self-statements and flow with your breathing and with a sense of yourself as a whole being? What happens to those thoughts when you do?

9. While you are exercising, be aware of messages that encourage you to stop or to back off your pace. Are these messages from your body or merely from your thinking? See if you can discriminate the real need to stop or slow down from the idea, which may be an exaggerated reaction to fatigue, boredom or discomfort.

10. While exercising, allow your eyes to become soft and unfocused so that your awareness is primarily of the rhythmic movements of your body and of light and color. Try this at times when you are feeling tired or fatigued.

MENTAL REHEARSAL AND SELF-SUGGESTION STRATEGIES

With awareness, concentration and relaxation as a foundation, you can begin to experiment with images to reinforce your physical training with particular intentions. In a state of deep relaxation, the neuromuscular system appears to accept such programs from the imagination. It has been shown that at rest, a runner visualizing himself running will actually have detectable firing of his major running muscles in the correct order. In a controlled experiment weightlifters who visualized their muscles getting bigger had increased testosterone levels compared to a control group who did not visualize as a part of their training. Golfer Jack Nicklaus claimed that for him hitting specific shots was 50 percent mental picture, 40 percent set-up and only 10 percent swing. Below is a much-quoted passage from *Golf My Way*, by Nicklaus and Ken Bowden, in which Nicklaus describes his use of imaging:

I never hit a shot, even in practice, without having a very sharp, in-focus picture of it in my head. It's like a color movie. First I "see" the ball where I want it to finish, nice and white and sitting up high on the bright green grass. Then the scene quickly changes and I "see" the ball going there—its path, trajectory, and shape, even its behavior on landing. Then there's a sort of fade-out, and the next scene shows me making the kind of swing that will turn the previous images into reality.

Mental images can be used in a variety of ways to support your performance. You can "image" a more confident you, a stronger you, a more technically precise you, a more graceful you during a specific performance or in general. Many individuals find these imaging exercises valuable and report that it is helpful to make the "scene" as vivid as possible with realistic details of light, color, setting, sounds, smells and so on. However, before you start the mental imaging or rehearsing, it is best to first go into a deep state of relaxed concentration with the meditation exercises.

Individual sports lend themselves to specific and precise mental rehearsal more than team sports do. A diver, a shooter, an archer, a gymnast, a weightlifter, a golfer can all image their ideal performing state and work on the details with great precision because the performing environment is relatively constant. The United States national archery teams now receive intensive training in imagery and relaxation as do many of our other national teams.

In team sports, in racing or in sports like tennis and the martial arts, a different, more flexible kind of imaging is required, one that emphasizes many possibilities and changing conditions. You can always rehearse mentally what you want to do and go out and attempt it. The pitfall is that if you have rehearsed only certain options and something else happens, you may be caught short. So the more complex the situation, in sports or in other activities, the more the mental rehearsal needs to be grounded in moment-to-moment awareness practices so that you remain in the present and are capable of responding to a changing situation even if it never occurred to you during your training sessions. To be a truly top performer in any arena, you need to train for the unexpected and the unanticipated. This is the work of awareness.

IMAGERY EXERCISES, MENTAL REHEARSAL AND COGNITIVE RESTRUCTURING

1. Runners: Visualize yourself as your favorite fast animal, say, an antelope or a cheetah. You can do this while running. Alternatively, visualize yourself as your favorite world-class runner and imitate his or her gait, style and facial expression. At other times, just practice visualizing these animals or pictures in as much detail as possible so that you can use them as cues in certain spots during your run when you feel yourself fading.

2. Cyclists and swimmers: Visualize your favorite cyclist or swimmer. Remember, the more detail the better. Swimmers can also think of animals if appropriate. The great Russian Olympic champion Vladimir Salnikov sometimes imagined there was a shark swimming after him. Be imaginative!

3. For any sport: Sit in meditation for a few minutes and then rehearse yourself performing your sport in your mind. You can choose one aspect, say, your backhand in tennis, and see yourself executing flawless backhands during a challenging match, or you can choose to go through an entire routine (say, in gymnastics or ice skating), again, executing with flawless technique and with relaxed concentration. As with any other skill, mental rehearsal improves with repetition and with as full a recreation as possible of the details of what the actual performance situation will be like. U.S. Olympic rowers Paul Enquist and Brad Lewis, who won the gold medal in 1984 in the double sculls, made good use of this kind of strategy. Part of their preparation involved putting one rowing machine (ergometer) behind another and then talking themselves through an entire "race," pulling on *imaginary* oar handles while moving back and forth on the seat exactly as if they were rowing. During this dynamic mental rehearsal, they shouted out particular phrases at key moments in the "race" to remind themselves of the way they wanted to look and feel, using as models the images of particular boats that had rowed memorable races they had viewed numerous times on videotape. They devised this mental strategy themselves and practiced it many times, in addition to all the more conventional forms of training, as they were preparing for the Olympic trials and later for the Olympics. As with any other skill, mental rehearsal improves with repetition.

In addition to imaging and mental rehearsal, it can also be very helpful to consciously modify your thinking and the labels you assign to opponents, in order to minimize the charge of particular elements of a situation, especially if you have already identified ways your thoughts and emotions are interfering with your chances of performing well. This process is called cognitive restructuring or reframing. A good example of its use comes from the 1983 America's Cup competition, in which the Australian team broke the 132-year hegemony of American teams. The Australians had to overcome two major obstacles: They were challenging the Americans in American territory, and none of the Australians knew what it was to win an America's Cup race. They were, as their skipper, John Bertrand, put it, "basically psyched out." In a speech reprinted in the Winter 1985 issue of *North News* magazine, Bertrand described how the Australians built confidence by relabeling their opponents.

> We just called [the other boat] "the red boat," or the "blue boat." We weren't trying to characterize the boats or the people . . . we'd heard . . . all the myths generated by the press about them. So we tried to make it all bland . . . In the end, we became so brash that we just called them "blue dog," and "red dog." The Aussies were coming of age, I assure you. It wasn't a public display; we weren't talking to the press [or] our supporters about this; we were talking within our own peer group on the boat to get the scales at least even.

By calling the American craft the "red boat" the Australians were able to diffuse much of the aura of invincibility around the American crew so that their own minds were less preoccupied with their competitors and the enormity of the stakes for them after three consecutive failures.

Most forms of cognitive restructuring involve shifting one's perspective to emphasize seeing obstacles as challenges and seeing the positive within the negative. As with imaging, cognitive restructuring can be very helpful in certain situations. It too, however, is best applied within the larger framework of meditative awareness. For example, many athletes practice seeing themselves winning and use autogenic statements and positive thoughts which emphasize their capacity to win. However, it is our feeling that learning to quiet one's mind and detach from all thoughts is an even more important skill than restructuring negative thoughts into positive ones. Even positive thoughts distract and drain one's energy, particularly if their content is beyond the possibility of control. Thus, having confidence that one can win in a competition is an indispensable ingredient in high performance. But thinking about what it will mean to win and how nice it will be is totally counterproductive until the result is actually achieved. What is required instead is moment-to-moment, concentrated attention to the relevant details of the situation. Again, an example from John Bertrand about the 1983 America's Cup:

> One of the areas we had to overcome was the feeling of incredible pressure on the crew and on myself. A lot of people have asked me how did I feel on a particular day . . . And how did we come from 3–1 down and so on . . . *We had to really*

close our minds off, and focus in . . . A lesson that I've really learned [from the Cup campaigns] *is that you can't really dwell on the negative or the positive of what you're trying to achieve. . . .* I could have burned up a lot of energy contemplating would it be worth coming back to Australia if we lost. That's number one. Or, conversely, what would it be like to come back to Australia if we won. Both those things . . . at that state of the campaign were totally counterproductive in trying to achieve that final result.

So I was very concerned that when we had our little team meetings, that *we just focus in on the day at hand and sail one day at a time.* If you're trying to achieve something, and you really want to achieve it, and there's a lot of pressure on you as a result—sometimes self-imposed or sometimes the result of your supporters, or the press, or, in this situation, the country—*you've really got to cut all of that out of your mind and just go ahead and give it your best shot. And don't dwell on the consequences of winning and losing.*

In this chapter we have given you a range of different specific exercises to use as part of an overall effort to get your mind to work for you rather than against you. The key to success in this domain is your own willingness to practice on a regular basis. Be willing to experiment and be creative, thereby making these exercises your own. Everybody's mind is different. You are in the best position to observe your own mind and to see how it influences your performance. Observe its workings carefully, learn to see clearly the thoughts, attitudes, and emotions that come up in your mind that are of no help but constantly subvert you, and practice letting go of them. Cultivate the state of relaxed concentration and awareness through regular practice, and see what happens.

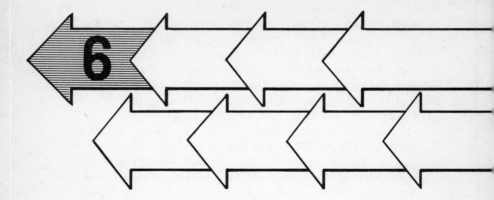

The staff of our Exercise Physiology Laboratory at the University of Massachusetts at Sports Medicine, Brookline, have counseled thousands of fitness enthusiasts, joggers, marathoners, dancers, wrestlers, football players, weightlifters, casual exercisers and Olympic athletes. Time and again, we hear the same story—"I know what foods I should eat, but I often don't choose them. I can't seem to combine healthy eating with my fast-paced lifestyle." Many of our clients feel guilty that they have committed "nutrition sins."

We recognize that eating healthfully on the run can be a challenge—but it is possible without being an incredible burden. The rewards of good health and overall fitness are worth the investment. What follows is an update on current nutrition controversies, along with suggestions for incorporating this information into wise food choices.

COFFEE

Coffee is the number-one beverage that instills guilt in the clients we've counseled. They're sure that it must be harmful to their health. While some people never touch coffee ("I'm so sensitive to the caffeine. It makes me very hyper and jittery"), others thrive on it ("I'm useless until I have some coffee to get me functioning—especially before I exercise.")

Coffee (as well as tea and cola) contains caffeine, a druglike stimulant. Thousands of research studies have tried to link coffee and caffeine to increased risks of developing cancer, hypertension, heart disease and diseases of aging. The current research indicates that for the healthy person, coffee in moderation (one to three cups a day) may not be as bad

NUTRITION

as some may think it is. For many of us, relaxing with a morning mug of coffee is a pleasant start for a busy day. However, a continuous intake of coffee—particularly coffee loaded with cream and sugar—may lead to health problems.

Certain people should abstain from drinking coffee. For example, if you combine your coffee drinking with cigarette smoking, you increase your risk of heart disease from the latter habit. Ulcer patients and others prone to stomach distress may find that coffee upsets their gastrointestinal system. Pregnant and breast-feeding women should avoid caffeine to prevent "stimulating" their infant.

But for the vast majority of Americans, the bigger culprit when it comes to your health may be the bad habits that surround this beverage:

- Opting for a coffee instead of a wholesome breakfast;
- Saturating the coffee with cream and sugar—nutritionally empty calories;
- Relying on coffee to keep you alert—rather than getting the sleep that you really need.

Regarding coffee and exercise performance, many athletes—particularly runners—use caffeine for a pre-exercise "perk me up." It seems to enhance their endurance as well as make the effort seem easier. In research studies by Ball State University's Dr. David Costill, runners who had caffeine (equivalent to two cups of coffee) an hour prior to exercise ran 15 minutes longer than when they exercised to exhaustion without the caffeine. In a second study, research subjects were instructed to cycle for 2 hours as hard as they could on a special bike which recorded the amount of energy they expended. They worked 7% harder when they had the caffeine, yet they perceived the effort with and without caffeine as being

Caffeine Content of Some Common Beverages

Beverage	mg/5-oz. cup
Coffee	
Drip	150
Percolated	110
Instant	65
Decaffeinated	5
Tea	
5-minute brew	45
1-minute brew	30
Cocoa	5
	mg/12-oz. can
Coke	65
Pepsi	45

Source: M. L. Bunker and M. McWilliams, "Caffeine Content of Common Beverages," Journal of the American Dietetic Association 74 (1979): 28.

the same. These studies provide suggestive evidence of what many runners believe—that coffee is a beverage of choice before hard exercise.

Although this research highlights the potential benefits of pre-exercise coffee, you should also be aware that coffee has its hazards. For one, caffeine has a dehydrating effect. It sends you running to the bathroom, where you lose fluids that could be more valuable to you during intense exercise, especially in hot weather. In a precompetition situation, coffee may overstimulate you at a time when you're already nervous and jittery. You may "burn out" and not perform at your best.

Bill Rodgers says he drinks coffee not for the "boost" but rather to empty the bowels before he runs. This insures a comfortable exercise session. Other athletes, however, may purposely avoid pre-exercise coffee in order to reduce the risk of unsolicited "pit stops." They find that coffee creates intestinal havoc.

As most health professionals will agree, a cup or two of coffee in moderation is undoubtedly the best advice for those who enjoy this brew. If you feel nervous, jittery and "caffeinated," however, you might want to drink decaffeinated beverages, such as decaffeinated coffee or tea, herbal tea, hot cider, broth and Grandmother's favorite—hot water with a lemon

---

Alcohol

You can get "loaded" with alcohol, but you can't load up your muscles with carbohydrates at the same time. The calories from beer, wine and whiskey come mostly from the alcohol content. They are not converted into glycogen stores.

Beverage	Amount	Calories
Beer	12-oz. can	150
Whiskey	1½-oz. jigger	105
Wine		
Champagne	4-oz. glass	84
Port	3½-oz. glass	158
Red table wine	3½-oz. glass	76
Sauterne	3½-oz. glass	84
Vermouth, dry	3½-oz. glass	150
White table wine	3½-oz. glass	80

Source: N. Clark, *The Athlete's Kitchen* (New York: Simon & Schuster, 1985), 246.

---

wedge. Or better yet, when you're at work and feeling droopy, enjoy an exercise break instead of a coffee break. Five or ten minutes of heart-stimulating walking is by far the healthiest way to perk yourself up!

BEER

Beer is often a beverage of choice for thirsty sports fans and adults in general. In fact, the 1984 market surveys showed that the "average American" consumes 24.3 gallons of beer per year. This translates into 260 cans. But, since one-third of Americans abstain from alcohol, that may actually translate into 350 cans of brew per year.

There's no doubt that alcohol is a depressant. When you're feeling "high" after a good workout, a beer can hit you like a ton of bricks—especially if you drink on an empty stomach. Although beer may be a popular choice for celebrating victories, it's actually better for killing pain.

Beer may be a popular beverage for thirsty sports fans, but it's certainly not the most appropriate beverage in terms of physiological needs.

Sodium Content of Some Common Foods

	Milligrams sodium		Milligrams sodium
Beverages		Ham, 3 oz.	1,100
Beer, 12 oz.	25	Tuna, 3 oz.	300
Coffee, 8 oz.	2		
Cola, 12 oz.	25	*Fruits*	
Cola, diet, 12 oz.	30	Apple, 1 medium	2
Orange juice, 8 oz.	5	Banana, 1 medium	2
Wine, 12 oz.	10	Cantaloupe, ¼	12
		Orange, 1 medium	1
Dairy Products			
Cheese, American,		*Condiments*	
1 oz.	400	Catsup, 1 tbsp.	175
Cheese, cheddar,		Mustard, 1 tsp.	65
1 oz.	175	Salt, 1 packet	500
Ice cream, 1 cup	75	Soy sauce, 1 tbsp.	1,350
Milk, whole or skim,			
1 cup	125	*Vegetables*	
Yogurt, fruit, 1 cup	130	Broccoli, 1 stalk	25
		Carrot, 1	35
Protein Foods		Celery, 1 stalk	25
Bacon, 2 slices	275	Lettuce, 1 cup	5
Beef, 3 oz. cooked	60	Peas, 1 cup fresh	2
Chicken, 1 breast	70	Peas, 1 cup frozen	80
Eggs, 1	60	Peas, 1 cup canned	500
Fish, 3 oz. raw	60		

Despite popular belief, beer is a poor source of carbohydrates, electrolytes and fluid. You may rationalize drinking a can or two of brew by thinking that it's the perfect fluid replacement, but you're wrong! You fool yourself when you try to "carbo-load" on beer. Of the 150 calories in a 12-ounce can, only 50 are from carbohydrates. (Light beer has even fewer carbohydrates.) Beer calories are primarily from alcohol and are thus a poor energy source for your muscles. You'll get "loaded" on beer but not carbo-loaded.

The primary reason that beer is a poor fluid replacement is that the alcohol has a diuretic effect that sends you hurrying to the bathroom, where you flush away valuable fluids. To recover best from hard exercise, you want to replace sweat losses, not lose more fluid. If after exercise you want a beer, we recommend that you first have two or three large glasses of water to replace your sweat losses. Then, if desired, relax with a beer.

Beer is also a poor source of the electrolytes lost in perspiration. You might lose 500 milligrams of sodium in a pound of perspiration. A beer

	Milligrams sodium		Milligrams sodium
Potato, baked,		*Nuts*	
1 medium	5	Peanut butter, 1 tbsp.	80
Tomato, 1 medium	15	Peanuts, salted,	
Tomato sauce, 1 cup	1,500	1 cup	990
V-8 juice, 1 cup	990	Walnuts, 1 cup	5
Cereals, Grains, Starches		*Fats and Oils*	
Bread, white, 1 slice	125	Butter, 1 tsp.	40
Cake, 1 slice	250	Margarine, 1 tsp.	45
Cereal, hot,		Mayonnaise, 1 tbsp.	75
1 oz. (dry)	5	Salad dressing, 1 tbsp.	120
Cereal, cold,			
1-oz. serving	250	*Canned Foods*	
Cookies, 1 Oreo	50	Soup, vegetable,	
Crackers, 2 saltines	70	1 cup	960
Doughnut,		Spaghetti, 1 cup	1,220
1 cake-type	160		
English muffin, 1	295		
Spaghetti, 1 cup			
unsalted	2		

Compiled by Nancy Clark, M.S., R.D., based on information in J. Pennington and H. Church, eds., *Food Values of Portions Commonly Used* (New York: Harper & Row, 1980).

would replace only 25 milligrams. As for potassium, you'd have to drink at least a whole six-pack to replace what you might sweat off during a marathon. Instead, guzzle a large (12-ounce) glass of potassium-rich orange juice to replace the losses.

SALT

Through the years, health professionals have deemed salt the culprit when it comes to high blood pressure. More recent data, however, indicate this charge may oversimplify an extremely complex issue. Nonetheless, if you have high blood pressure or a family history of it, you are best advised to restrict your salt intake.

Even if you don't salt your food, you'll get plenty through the foods you eat. The typical American diet contains six to ten times the amount of salt you need. If you need additional salt, your body will send out a

Potassium Content of Some Common Foods

The suggested daily intake for potassium is 2,600 milligrams for the average person and 6,000 for the athlete not acclimated to the heat who loses potassium through sweat. The typical American diet contains 4,000–7,000 milligrams of potassium per day. One pound of sweat loss may contain 85–105 milligrams.

	Milligrams potassium		Milligrams potassium
Fruits		Peas, ¼ cup cooked	125
Apple, 1 medium	165	Pepper, green,	
Banana, 1 small 6″	370	1 large raw	315
Cantaloupe, ¼ of 5″		Potato, baked,	
melon	250	1 medium	750
Orange, 1 medium 3″	300	Spinach, ½ cup	
Pear, 1 medium	65	cooked	290
Prunes, 5 dried	350	Tomato sauce,	
Raisins, 2 tbsp.	150	½ cup canned	590
Vegetables		*Protein Foods*	
Beans, green, 1 cup		Chicken, white meat,	
cooked	190	3.5 oz.	410
Broccoli, 1 stalk		Chicken, dark meat,	
cooked	270	3.5 oz.	320
Carrot, 1 large raw	340	Egg, 1 medium	60
Lettuce, iceberg,		Fish, haddock,	
1 wedge raw	265	3.5 oz.	355
Mushrooms, 4 large		Hamburger,	
raw	415	3.5 oz. lean	480

warning signal in the form of a "salt craving." For example, many marathoners and triathletes tend to seek out salty chips, crackers and pretzels after exercise.

Some athletes believe they should take salt tablets to replace sweat losses. They shouldn't. Salt tablets are unnecessary and even potentially dangerous. They further dehydrate you by pulling water from your body tissues into your stomach to dilute the high concentration of sodium (the part of salt that you lose in sweat) from the tablet.

Your first concern after a sweaty workout should be to replace the water you've lost, since the concentration of sodium in your blood actually increases during exercise. As you become dehydrated, you perspire proportionately more water than sodium. When you eat, you'll undoubtedly replace the salt. The foods that Americans commonly choose after exercise (muffins, pancakes, yogurt, crackers, cheese, soup, pizza) contain significant amounts of sodium. Even if you add no salt to your food, you

	Milligrams potassium		Milligrams potassium
Peanut butter, 2 tbsp.	250	*Dairy Products*	
		Ice cream, 1 cup	220
Tuna, ½ cup	280	Milk, 1 cup whole or low-fat	380
Cereals, Grains, Starch		Yogurt, 1 cup whole or low-fat	380
Beans, kidney, ½ cup canned	350	Cheese, American, 1 oz.	20
Bran flakes, 1 cup	135	Cheese, cheddar, 1 oz.	25
Bread, white, 1 slice	25	Cheese, mozzarella, 1 oz.	20
Bread, whole wheat, 1 slice	65		
Cornflakes, 1 cup	25	*Beverages*	
Flour, white, 1 cup	105	Apple juice, 1 cup	240
Flour, whole wheat, 1 cup	445	Beer, 12 oz.	90
Oatmeal, ⅓ cup dry	95	Coke, 12 oz.	5
Rice, white, ¼ cup raw	45	Cranberry juice, 1 cup	25
Rice, brown, ¼ cup raw	105	Gatorade, 1 cup	25
Spaghetti, 1 cup cooked	115	Orange juice, 1 cup	420

Compiled by Clark, based on information in Pennington and Church, eds., *Food Values of Portions Commonly Used.*

may still consume 2,000–3,000 milligrams—more than enough to satisfy your needs.

Your body also helps by adapting to your natural intake. The less salt you eat, the less you'll sweat. The more salt you eat, the more you'll sweat.

POTASSIUM

In contrast to the "nutritional no-nos," potassium is one nutrient that's positive and protective of your health. Pile on the potassium! According to the latest research, potassium may

• reduce your risk of developing high blood pressure;

• keep your arteries healthy and better able to withstand damage that might lead to stroke and kidney disease.

Potassium is found in the majority of wholesome foods—fruits, vegetables, whole-grain breads, lentils, beans, nuts and lean meats. If you're eating on the run, you may have a low potassium intake. However, you can easily boost it by following these suggestions:

• Choose whole wheat, rye and dark breads instead of white bread and refined grain products. For example, a cup of whole wheat flour has about 450 milligrams of potassium, as compared to a cup of white flour with only 100 milligrams.
• Eat generous servings of vegetables. Since vegetables lose some potassium during cooking, you'll be better off with steamed, microwave-cooked or stir-fried vegetables, as compared to overcooked mushy ones. If you frequently eat out, Chinese restaurants can offer you the crispy vegetables that contribute to your good health.
• For a change from fast-food burgers, try a salad filled with colorful, potassium-rich vegetables such as green peppers, tomatoes and carrots. Salad bars are a convenient way to quickly boost your potassium intake.
• Opt for potatoes rather than rice or noodles. Potatoes are among the richest sources of potassium—750 milligrams per 3-inch potato. A cup of spaghetti, on the other hand, has only 115 milligrams.
• Snack on fresh and dried fruits, especially bananas, oranges and prunes.

By increasing your potassium intake, you'll not only reduce your risk of high blood pressure, you'll also be consuming many fiber-rich, low-fat heart-healthful foods that will positively influence your overall health.

CALCIUM

Make no bones about it—milk and other calcium sources are as important for adults as for growing children. Not only may calcium protect you from hypertension, but it also helps to guard your bone strength. Your bones are alive and need 800–1,500 milligrams of calcium per day to keep strong. Keep in mind that bones don't reach their peak density until you're 30 to 35 years old. The amount of bone mass that you have at this age is the single most important factor influencing your susceptibility to fractures as you get older.

Calcium Equivalents

These foods, in the quantities indicated, contain approximately the same amount of calcium as 8 ounces of whole milk.

Buttermilk	1 cup
Cheese, cheddar	1½ oz.
Cheese, cottage	2 cups
Cheese, processed	1½ slices
Yogurt	1 cup
Ice cream	1½ cups
Ice milk	1½ cups
Tofu	9 oz.
Broccoli	1½ cups
Collard or turnip greens	2 cups
Kale or mustard greens	1 cup
Oysters	1½ cups (about 16 medium)
Salmon	4 oz.
Sardines	2½ oz.

Compiled by Clark, based on information in Pennington and Church, eds. *Food Values of Portions Commonly Used.*

Osteoporosis—thinning of the bones with age—is due in part to calcium-poor diets. This prevalent national health problem afflicts at least 15 million Americans, including 25% of women over 65. Osteoporosis is becoming increasingly problematic as we live to be older and older. We can reduce its incidence by eating calcium-rich foods throughout our lives.

To increase your intake of this protective nutrient, you should consume some dairy products at least twice a day. Low-fat products, such as low-fat yogurt, skim milk and part-skim mozzarella cheese, are the preferable choices. Here are some suggestions for including these calcium-rich foods:

- Eat cereal with milk for breakfast. If you have an aversion to soggy cereal, replace milk with yogurt and enjoy the crunch.
- When eating fast foods, choose pizza with calcium-rich, part-skim mozzarella cheese. Or add cheese (preferably low-fat, if available) to sandwiches.
- Drink low-fat milk instead of soft drinks at lunch and dinner. If you have trouble digesting milk, try Lact-aid, the lactose-free brand that's available at larger supermarkets.
- Toss together calcium-rich salads by adding grated cheese, low-fat

cottage cheese and yogurt dressing (made by adding salad seasonings to plain yogurt).
• Choose calcium-rich desserts such as frozen yogurt, ice milk and pudding, preferably made with skim milk. Note that ice cream, although made from dairy products, is a marginal source of calcium for the calories—but (unfortunately) an exceptional source of fat and cholesterol.

In addition to a calcium-rich diet, you'll help to maintain bone strength by regular weight-bearing exercises, such as walking, jogging and dancing. This diet-and-exercise combination again reinforces the fact that good health stems from a combination of many aspects of your lifestyle.

SUGAR AND SWEETS

Sugar in any form—white sugar, maple syrup, honey—is a simple carbohydrate that is easily digested and readily fuels your muscles. Two problems with sugar are that it has little nutritional value and it contributes to dental caries.

Despite common belief, the body uses the energy from natural sugars in fruits the same way it uses the refined sugar from candy. The primary difference is that fruits supply nourishing vitamins and minerals along with the sugar calories, while sweets do not. Eating a lot of sugar and goo is the equivalent to putting gas in the car but neglecting to replace the spark plugs.

Many active people consume vast quantities of chocolate chip cookies, ice cream and soft drinks as "rewards" for exercise. If you do eat sweets, first eat wholesome meals, then have a dessert, if desired. Too many dieters and exercisers "save calories" by skipping breakfast, then ravenously devour two candy bars at 10:30 A.M. when they are "dying of starvation." They could have better eaten those calories in the form of a nutritious bowl of cereal with milk and sliced banana.

In some cases, sweets can fit appropriately into a well-balanced diet. For example, if you've had a satisfying soup, sandwich and milk for lunch but still hanker for something sweet, your diet can better accommodate this treat and still provide you with the nutrients you need for top performance. High school football players who chow down on 5,000 calories a day can afford 250 calories of a candy bar, if eaten as a "fun food" rather than as a "first food."

Be aware that most "goodies" are loaded with fat and cholesterol—

Sweets with Some Nutritional Value

Apple crisp
Banana split with nuts
Carrot cake
Chocolate-covered peanuts
Date bars
Maple-walnut ice cream
Oatmeal-raisin cookies
Peanut brittle
Popcorn balls
Pumpkin pie
Sesame candy

Source: Clark, *The Athlete's Kitchen,* 226.

---

the culprits when it comes to heart disease. Even exercise enthusiasts are susceptible to heart disease and should be concerned about their intake of heart-unhealthful foods.

As far as sugar being a source of pre-exercise quick energy, a "sugar fix" taken 30–45 minutes beforehand can have a negative effect. Sweets may actually hurt your performance by contributing to hypoglycemia (low blood sugar). Sugary foods, such as soft drinks, candy, even juices, cause your blood sugar to rise. Your body responds by releasing insulin, a hormone that carries the sugar away from your blood and into your cells. Exercise, like insulin, enhances this transfer of sugar out of the blood. Hence, when you exercise after having eaten many sweets, the insulin/exercise combination may remove too much sugar, making you feel shaky, weak, tired and perhaps uncoordinated. You certainly will have a poorer workout than if you had simply had a few crackers, a piece of toast or some other sugar-free pre-exercise snack. These starchy foods will take the edge off your appetite, digest into sugar and provide you with the energy you need—without the hampering side effects. You don't have to eat sugar to get sugar into your system.

We recommend wholesome, natural sweets like fruits and juices over candy bars and soft drinks.

JUNK FOOD

The term "junk food" is actually a misnomer. It loosely describes any food with little nutritional value compared to the calories it offers such as the omnipresent grease and goo lurking through America. In reality, however, any food—even apples—can become a junk food if eaten in excess. We need to eat a variety of wholesome foods—fruits, vegetables, unprocessed grains, low-fat proteins—to fuel ourselves with premium nutrition. No one food will offer us every nutrient that we need. Nor will any one food ruin our health.

Rather than looking at junk food, consider the concept of a "junk diet." We worry less about the person who has an occasional doughnut or cookie than we do about the one who lives on ice cream for dinner because he or she is too lazy to cook a nourishing meal or the crash dieter who skips meals but then "blows it" by eating a whole bag of Oreos. These people are getting very few of the vitamins, minerals and protein they need for exercising at their best and investing in their health.

Rather than dwell on junk food and feel guilty when you eat an ice cream sundae, you might better think of some foods as being "fun foods." Fun foods have little nutritional value but simply add to life's enjoyment. They are neither "good" nor "bad." In excess they compile into a junk diet. But if you first eat wholesome foods and then have a treat for fun, you can still have a well-balanced diet. *Moderation* is the best advice.

FAST FOODS

Nutritionally speaking, fast-food meals can be adequate if you choose wisely. For example, pizza with low-fat mozzarella cheese, green peppers, mushrooms and onions is a well-balanced meal incorporating many of the nutrients you need for good health. (Just eliminate the pepperoni and sausage toppings.) Fried-fish sandwiches smothered with tartar sauce, greasy double bacon cheeseburgers and French fries are another story. They're loaded with fat—the major problems with fast foods. In five minutes you can easily consume a lot of "cloggage" and more than half the calories you need for the entire day. A mere burger, shake and fries can total up to 1,000 calories. That's asking for weight control problems. Fast foods may also lack fiber and vitamins A and C and have excessive amounts of salt.

When you eat fast foods, plan to balance that meal with the rest of the day's intake. Have a low-fat breakfast of orange juice (vitamin C) and bran cereal (fiber). Tuck an apple into your pocket for a dessert alternative to apple pie. Instead of having a cola for an afternoon break, enjoy a can of V-8. If you have high blood pressure, choose low-salt foods for your other meals. Scout out the area for fast-and-healthful alternatives to the fast-and-fatty ones; bran muffins, turkey sandwiches, vegetable-soup-to-go, bananas are all delicious possibilities. Keep an "emergency food supply" of stoned-wheat crackers in your desk drawer. With a little bit of thought, you can conveniently, healthfully and enjoyably nourish yourself with the foods that invest in your well-being and top performance.

CARBOHYDRATES

As a sports enthusiast, you may know that carbohydrates are the best source of fuel for your muscles. But as a person concerned about your weight, you may think that carbohydrates are fattening, and hesitate to eat them.

Carbohydrates are the best energy source for sports enthusiasts. And carbohydrates are *not* fattening. They supply 4 calories per gram, as compared to fats, which offer more than twice that amount—9 calories per gram. Carbohydrates generally combine with fats, such as butter on bread, sour cream on potato, oil in Chinese fried rice—and that's when they become "fattening." If you want to lose weight, you should eat the carbohydrates for energy but eliminate the fats. That way you'll have the energy to exercise but the lower caloric intake to lose weight.

Carbohydrates include both sugars and starches. The sugars (table sugar, honey, maple syrup, and fruit sugars) are often referred to as "simple sugars" because they are comprised of one or two molecules that digest easily and convert into glucose. Starches (potatoes, wheat, rice), on the other hand, are often referred to as "complex carbohydrates" because they are bigger molecules and take longer to digest. Starches are actually a chain of sugar molecules hooked together, similar to a string of pearls, with each pearl being a single molecule of sugar.

Plants convert excess sugars into starch. For example, corn on the cob, which is sweet when it's young, becomes starchy as it gets older. People also convert extra dietary sugars into starch—more commonly referred to as glycogen. We store this glycogen in our muscles. It's readily available for quick energy when we exercise.

As an exercise enthusiast, you should try to consume at least half of your calories—if not more—from carbohydrates. The trick is to eat more naturally occurring sugars, such as those in fruits and juices, and un-

Fast-Food Calories

Fast foods are typically fatty, salty and calorie-laden; they tend to be poor sources of fiber, vitamins A and C. You should try to balance out a fast-food lunch by including fruits, vegetables and other wholesome low-fat foods in the rest of your daily meals and snacks.

	Calories		Calories
McDonald's		*Burger King*	
Hamburger	255	Hamburger	290
Cheeseburger	300	Whopper Junior	370
Quarter Pounder with		Whopper	630
cheese	525	Whopper with cheese	740
Big Mac	565	Whaler	745
Chicken McNuggets, 6	315	Onion rings	270
Filet-O-Fish	430	Chocolate shake	340
French fries	220		
Apple pie	355	*Kentucky Fried Chicken*	
McDonaldland cookies	310	2 pieces, original recipe	395
Hot fudge sundae	310	2 pieces, extra crispy	545
Vanilla shake	310	2-piece dinner, original	
Chocolate shake	385	recipe	660
English muffin with		2-piece dinner, extra	
butter	185	crispy	900
Egg McMuffin	325		
Hotcakes with butter			
and syrup	500		
Scrambled egg			
breakfast	700		

processed starches, such as whole wheat bread and brown rice. These unrefined carbohydrates have more nutritional value and provide not only energy, but also the vitamins and minerals that contribute to your optimal health and top performance. Carbohydrates are definitely friends and not the fattening, empty-calorie culprits they've been reputed to be.

FATS

Fats are the culprits when it comes to obesity, heart disease, cancer and other diseases of aging. Fats are concentrated calories, with little nutritional value. According to the Pritikin Diet, you should eliminate all animal fats from your diet to reduce dramatically your risk of developing heart disease. While this approach is perhaps the best, the strictness can

	Calories		Calories
Pizza Hut		*Sandwich Fixings*	
½ 13″ pizza, cheese	680	Breads	
½ 13″ pizza supreme	800	Most types, 2 slices	140
		Syrian, ½ 8″ pocket	120
Dunkin' Donuts		Submarine roll, large	460
Munchkin, raised	35	Condiments, per tbsp.	
Munchkin, cake-type	50	Butter or margarine	100
Plain, cake-type	275	Mayonnaise	100
Honey-dipped, raised	225	Miracle Whip	60
Coffee roll, honey-		Weight Watcher's	
dipped	330	mayonnaise	40
Muffin, blueberry	280	Fillings (per oz.)	
Muffin, bran	320	Turkey roll	35
Coffee with cream and		Turkey breast	50
sugar	70	Roast beef, lean	55
		Ham	65
		Hamburger	75
		Bologna	90
		Cheese	110
		Liverwurst	140
		Peanut butter,	
		2 tbsp.	180
		Jelly	100

Compiled by Clark, based on information from the restaurants and in Pennington and Church, eds., *Food Values of Portions Commonly Used.*

be unrealistic for Americans eating on the run. According to an article in the May 1984 issue of the *Journal of the American Dietetic Association,* a moderate-fat diet (25–30% of your daily calories) is almost as effective as a Pritikin-type very low fat diet (14% of your daily calories). Subjects who followed the one-year dietary program showed an 8% drop in serum cholesterol on the moderate fat intake, as compared to a 10% drop on the Pritikin-type program.

If sticking with the rules of a fat-reduced diet is sometimes unrealistic for you, keep in mind that some fats are more acceptable than others. Polyunsaturated fats—that is, the liquid vegetable oils such as corn, sunflower, safflower—are acceptable additions to your diet (if you can afford the calories). They are more healthful than the saturated animal fats—hard butter, lard and beef tallow.

You can shift your intake from saturated animal fats to polyunsaturated fats simply by cooking with oil instead of butter and substituting

Definitions: Fat and Cholesterol

Fatty acids are grouped in three families: saturated, monosaturated and polyunsaturated. Each fatty acid molecule consists of atoms of carbon (C), hydrogen (H) and oxygen (O), arranged in a specific pattern.

When there is a hydrogen atom at every available spot in the molecule, the fatty acid is saturated. It is holding all the hydrogen that is possible; its chemical structure looks like this (R represents the rest of the chain in the following diagrams):

```
        H     H     H     H     H    OH
        |     |     |     |     |     |
  R  —  C  —  C  —  C  —  C  —  C  —  C  =  O
        |     |     |     |     |
        H     H     H     H     H
```

When some hydrogen is missing, the molecule is not saturated; it is unsaturated. If just one molecule of hydrogen is missing, the fatty acid is monosaturated. Olive oil is a monosaturated fat.

```
        H     H     H     H     H     H     H    OH
        |     |     |     |     |     |     |     |
  R  —  C  =  C  —  C  —  C  —  C  —  C  —  C  —  C  =  O
        |     |     |     |     |
        H     H     H     H     H
```

If two or more molecules of hydrogen are missing, the molecule is polyunsaturated. Corn oil is a polyunsaturated fat.

```
        H     H     H     H     H     H     H    OH
        |     |     |     |     |     |     |     |
  R  —  C  =  C  —  C  —  C  —  C  =  C  —  C  —  C  =  O
        |     |                             |
        H     H                             H
```

other vegetable oils for animal fats, such as using peanut butter rather than butter. Often food processors convert the soft or liquid polyunsaturated fats into solids, as happens with margarine and some brands of peanut butter. During this hardening process, called hydrogenation, the oils are saturated with hydrogen molecules. They become as unhealthful as other saturated animal fats. For this reason, "all-natural" peanut butter is a better choice than the harder, processed types.

For weight watchers, fats of any type are the culprits. Butter, margarine, oil, salad dressing, gravy, grease, fried foods—all are sources of concentrated calories. If you are fueling yourself for exercise by carbo-

Fatty acids travel in the blood in the form of triglycerides. Three fatty acid chains attach to a molecule of glycerol to form a tri- (meaning "three") glyceride.

Cholesterol is not a member of the fatty acid family. It has a different chemical structure, and is not used for energy.

loading on buttered bread, be aware that you may be fat-loading and contributing to weight gain rather than energizing your muscles. If you fill up on fats, you'll displace the carbohydrates, the better energy source for your muscles. You're better off focusing on low-fat carbohydrates. You'll have the energy to run and burn off the excess body fat that too easily accumulates when you eat lots of grease and goo.

You can eliminate as much fat as possible without fear of becoming fat-deficient. You'll undoubtedly get the small amount of fat that's essential for good health, since most foods naturally contain a small amount of fat.

Cholesterol Content of Some Common Foods

So you want to eat less cholesterol? Start by limiting your intake of these foods. You should try to eat no more than 250–300 milligrams cholesterol a day.

Beef liver, 3 oz.	372 mg
1 egg	274 mg
Sardines, 3 oz.	129 mg
Mackerel, 3 oz.	85 mg
Veal, 3 oz.	85 mg
Lamb, 3 oz.	83 mg
Hamburger, 3 oz.	80 mg
Pork, 3 oz.	80 mg
Lean beef, 3 oz.	77 mg
Chicken, 3 oz.	76 mg
Lobster, 3 oz.	62 mg
Turkey, 3 oz.	60 mg
Ice cream, 1 cup	59 mg
Hot dog, 3 oz.	52 mg
Haddock, 3 oz.	51 mg

Source: Pennington and Church, eds., *Food Values of Portions Commonly Used.*

CHOLESTEROL

Unlike fat, cholesterol is not burned for energy. Instead, cholesterol is a part of cell walls in animal foods, such as meat, eggs and even chicken and fish. Your body makes cholesterol. It has been confirmed that people with a high blood cholesterol level do have a significantly higher risk of developing heart disease. The cholesterol accumulates in the walls of the blood vessels throughout the body—and especially those vessels in the heart. This buildup limits blood flow to the heart muscle and contributes to heart attacks.

The American Heart Association recommends that Americans reduce this risk by limiting their dietary cholesterol intake to less than 300 milligrams per day and—perhaps more important—by conscientiously reducing their intake of the saturated fats we described.

Although exercise can increase the level of your HDL cholesterol (a good type of cholesterol that helps transport the bad cholesterol out of your body), exercise can also increase your intake of heart-unhealthful reward foods. Too many athletes treat themselves to a greasy pepperoni pizza, chips, ice cream, cookies and other high-fat/high-cholesterol foods after a hard workout.

Research with racing cyclists on a high-fat diet showed that they still had high blood cholesterol levels, despite their rigorous exercise program. When they ate low-fat, healthful foods, their cholesterol levels dropped. This study emphasizes the fact that even though exercise can be good for your health, it doesn't override what you eat.

By combining a diet low in cholesterol and saturated fats, you can reduce your blood cholesterol levels and your risk of developing heart disease. Exercise can enhance your health, unless you confound the positive exercise-induced increases of HDL cholesterol with a careless diet of fat- and cholesterol-rich foods.

Vegetarian Diets

Without a doubt, vegetarians can follow diets that provide adequate amounts of protein and other nutrients to support a vigorous exercise program and maintain their health. The racehorse is just one example of a vegetarian athlete. If you focus your meals on beans, lentils, grains and other vegetable sources of protein, not only can you obtain sufficient protein to build and maintain muscles, but you can also increase your intake of muscle-energizing carbohydrates.

Ideally, the vegetarian diet can be more healthful (that is, higher in carbohydrates and fiber, lower in saturated fat and cholesterol) than the typical fatty, meat-based American diet. However, many vegetarians trade in greasy burgers and juicy steaks for cholesterol/fat–laden cheese omelets, casseroles with rich cheese sauces and whole wheat breads slathered with butter. They neglect the fact that fat—more than protein—is the culprit when it comes to heart disease. If you choose to eat a vegetarian diet for health reasons, we recommend that you be consistent and choose healthful alternatives such as low-fat yogurt, milk and cheeses, and cook with recommended oils, such as olive, corn, sunflower and safflower.

Although vegetarians can get adequate amounts of protein, they may have a deficient intake of iron—a mineral important for transporting oxygen to your muscles. Although vegetables, beans, grains and other vegetarian foods provide some iron, the iron is generally poorly absorbed. You can enhance this absorption by including a vitamin C–rich food (such as orange juice, green peppers, broccoli, potatoes) along with each meal to enhance iron absorption. Cooking in a cast-iron skillet is another way to increase your iron intake, as is selecting iron-enriched breads, cereals, pastas and grains.

Vegetarians can have a health-promoting diet that sustains a high

---

Foods Rich in Vitamin C

These foods, in the amounts indicated, supply 100% of the recommended dietary allowance (RDA = 60 mg vitamin C):

Broccoli	1 stalk
Cabbage, raw	1 cup
Cantaloupe	½ medium
Green pepper	½ medium
Orange juice	6 oz.
Potato, baked	1 large
Strawberries, frozen	½ cup
Tomatoes	2 medium

Source: Clark, *The Athlete's Kitchen*, 135.

---

level of activity. By carefully combining a variety of beans, grains and legumes, they can get sufficient protein. Their bigger concern may be iron deficiency—and too much fat and cholesterol.

VITAMIN SUPPLEMENTS

Vitamins regulate the biochemical reactions within your body. They are chemical substances that your body cannot manufacture. Thus you must obtain them through the foods you eat.

Although it seems logical that an active person would need more vitamins than a sedentary person, the research to date shows no direct evidence of a dramatically increased use, destruction or excretion of vitamins in association with hard training, other than the requirement for B vitamins involved in converting food into energy.

Vitamins are like spark plugs in a car. A few extras won't make your engine run stronger. Excessive amounts of vitamins will not increase performance, strength or energy. Nevertheless, many energy seekers spend their food budgets on vitamins. You could spend that money better on wholesome foods—oranges, broccoli, whole wheat bread, low-fat yogurt, for instance. You can get the vitamins you need from the foods you eat, assuming that you live on more than "reward foods"—cookies, candy, soft drinks and other nutritionally poor choices.

Although excessive amounts of vitamins will not enhance your performance, a lack of vitamins may interfere with your ability to function at your best. If you question the adequacy of your diet, you might want to see a registered dietitian (R.D.). This nutrition professional will assess your food choices and help you to optimize your intake within the framework of your food preferences and lifestyle. You'll be better off in the long run investing your money in professional guidance than in vitamin supplements. After all, food is more than vitamins—it is energy, health and performance. Since a supplement may contain only five or ten of the more than fifty nutrients that are essential to your good health, you still have to eat well—even if you take a supplement.

FIBER

Dietary fiber is the part of plant cells that humans can't digest. We most generally correlate fiber with "bowel control." Fiber absorbs water, increases fecal bulk and consequently has a laxative effect. You'll tend to have regular bowel movements if you eat a high-fiber diet.

Fiber may also be a hero when it comes to reducing the risk of colon cancer. Fiber can triple stool volume, thereby diluting the concentration of bile acids (substances that help digest fat and are suspected cancer instigators). Some researchers believe that bile acids irritate the intestinal lining, leaving it open to attack from carcinogens. They recommend that you eat a high-fiber, low-fat diet to reduce your risk of developing colon cancer.

Fiber's health benefits vary according to the type of fiber you eat. Not all fibers are created equal. The fiber in whole grains such as whole wheat, corn meal and brown rice increases fecal bulk and reduces intestinal problems such as constipation, diverticulosis and colon cancer. Oat fiber tends to lower serum cholesterol. Hence, if you have a family history of heart disease, you might want to eat oat bran (available as a hot cereal) for breakfast. Some studies show that oat bran significantly lowers serum cholesterol by as much as 15–25% when combined with a low-fat diet. Pectin, another type of fiber, may help lower blood cholesterol and also control blood sugar in diabetics.

Americans who eat on the run commonly have a low fiber intake because they include few fruits, vegetables and unrefined grain products in their fast-food choices. You can boost your fiber intake by eating a bran muffin instead of a doughnut, bran cereals instead of bacon and eggs, whole wheat breads instead of bulky rolls. In general, you should try to focus your diet on wholesome fiber-rich foods—fresh fruits and vegetables, whole wheat breads and unrefined grains. They'll contribute not only more health-promoting fiber but also vitamins and minerals. The more "whole" and unprocessed a food is, the better it tends to be for you.

High-Fiber Foods

Fiber is the part of plants that cannot be digested by man. An adequate intake of fiber promotes regular bowel movements. Fiber absorbs water, which makes the stools softer and easier to eliminate. Drinking several glasses of liquids daily and exercising regularly will also promote regular elimination.

Fiber is lost through food processing, such as milling whole wheat into white flour, peeling skins from fruits and vegetables, pureeing, straining and juicing. Choose foods in their natural state if possible. Here is a list of foods with the corresponding dietary fiber content:

1 slice whole wheat bread	2 g
1 slice white bread	.5 g
1 medium apple	3.5 g
½ cup applesauce	2.6 g
1 medium orange	5 g
½ cup orange juice	0 g

Bran is the most concentrated source of fiber. Other good sources are nuts, seeds, grains, fruits and vegetables. The recommended daily intake is 20–35 grams.

Eating bran cereals is an easy way to increase your fiber intake. You can sprinkle raw bran on cereals, salads or entrees or eat bran cereals such as those listed below with their corresponding dietary fiber content.

All-Bran, 1 oz. (⅓ cup)	9 g
Bran flakes, 1 oz. (⅔ cup)	4 g
Fruit & Fibre, 1 oz. (½ cup)	3 g

Breads made from whole-grain flours—wheat, rye, oats—are high in fiber. Bran breads and bran muffins are excellent choices. The following list gives amounts of dietary fiber in 1 slice of each of the types of breads.

Cracked wheat	2 g
Whole wheat	2 g
Pumpernickel	1 g
Rye	1 g
White	.5 g

Fresh and dried fruits with edible seeds or skins are high in fiber.

Fresh

Orange, 1 medium	5 g
Pear, 1 medium	5 g
Raspberries, ½ cup	4.5 g
Banana, 1 medium	4 g
Apple, 1 medium	3.5 g
Strawberries, ½ cup	2 g

Dried

Prunes, 6	6 g
Apricots, 6	5 g
Figs, 2	5 g
Dates, 5	3 g
Raisins, ¼ cup	3 g

Vegetables in general, especially those with edible skins and seeds, are high in fiber. The difference in fiber between raw and cooked vegetables is insignificant. Note that lettuce is a low-fiber vegetable. (Unless otherwise specified, the fiber content listed is for ½ cup cooked of each vegetable.)

Spinach	5.5 g
Corn	4 g
Peas	4 g
Broccoli	3 g
Turnips	3 g
Carrot, 1 medium raw or ½ cup cooked	2.5 g
Eggplant	2.5 g
Cabbage	2 g
Green beans	2 g
Tomato, 1 medium raw	2 g
Lettuce, ⅙ head	1.5 g
Cauliflower	1 g
Celery, raw, 1 stalk	1 g
Green pepper, 1 medium raw	1 g

Beans and legumes, such as lentils and split peas, are excellent sources of fiber as well as protein. Meat, chicken, fish, eggs and dairy sources of protein are poor sources of fiber.

Baked beans, 1 cup	21 g
Split peas, 1 cup cooked	21 g
Chili with beans, 1 cup	19 g
Lentils, 1 cup cooked	18 g

Nuts and seeds are good high-fiber snacks, as are baked goods containing dried fruits and nuts.

Almonds, ¼ cup	5 g
Peanuts, ¼ cup	3 g
Peanut butter, 2 tbsp.	2.5 g

Low-fiber foods include meat, chicken, fish, eggs, milk, cheese, sugar, candy, sweets, butter, margarine, oil, salad dressing, gravy and fat.

Conclusion

Food is more than fuel. Food is energy, nourishment, health and, most certainly, enjoyment. Wise food choices on a day-to-day basis build a foundation for your future well-being. That's why we have made nutrition one of our 7 Building Blocks for total fitness. Although maintaining the high-fiber, low-fat wholesome diet that you know you should keep may sometimes be unrealistic, you can at least make the effort to balance your day's and week's eating so that the trend is toward optimal nutrition. This nourishing diet, in addition to the other building blocks we describe, will help you reach your total fitness goals.

If you struggle with nutritional concerns and cannot easily put into practice the healthful suggestions outlined above, we urge you to consult with a registered dietitian. This nutrition professional will teach you realistic guidelines that will help you to lose weight successfully, consume the nutrients you need via food rather than supplements, and focus on your personal eating concerns—whether you are a traveling businessman experiencing "creeping obesity" because of lavish restaurant eating or a vegetarian weightlifter who wants to bulk up. To locate a registered dietitian, call the nutrition clinic at your local hospital or your state's dietetic association, or look in the yellow pages. For professional credibility, be sure to select a name followed by the initials "R.D." As you know, good nutrition is a sound investment.

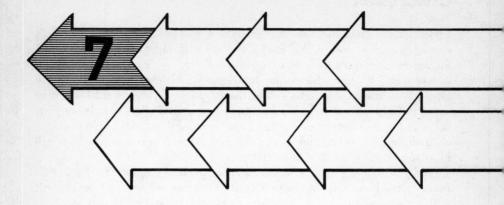

A comprehensive approach to training will help you perform your best and lessen your chance of injury. Initially, you and your trainer, coach or health professional should set realistic goals. Your training program should provide for progressive improvement. Once your program is developed, you *must* stick to it.

A good training program will include all of the building blocks previously discussed and make them work for you. Through adherence to this training program, it is possible for a successful athlete to maintain a higher level of achievement and influence his or her own career. The results of such a planned training program obviously benefit the athlete's team and family, as well as all extended personal and business relationships.

The training period must begin *before* you start participating in a sport. You should develop the strength, flexibility and cardiac and muscle endurance necessary for the activity. We see the greatest number of avoidable injuries in high school and collegiate athletes in September because many athletes believe they have followed a training program during the summer and return to practice within a mere two weeks of when they are scheduled for competition. The intensity of their activity suddenly increases, and those who have only moderately prepared begin to experience muscle aches, muscle strains, avulsions and stress fractures.

The time to start a training program depends on your current physical condition and the physical demands of the event for which you are training. Obviously there are certain age and physical features that may modify your preparation. The principle of training is to achieve *s*pecific *a*daptation to *i*mposed *d*emands (the SAID concept). In general, one must plan a minimum of six weeks of well-planned training to achieve an improvement in physical readiness. Some highly skilled athletes seeking

TRAINING

success in Olympic competition may plan up to three years of training for events that will be completed in seconds or minutes. A major-league baseball player must plan his year-long lifestyle alongside his training program if he is to remain an active and successful athlete.

The training program must include nutrition; flexibility; strength, power and endurance; tissue endurance; aerobic conditioning; speed improvement; stress reduction; and mental strategies. Each of these areas must be considered individually when determining the right program for you and the activity you have chosen. There is no single program that prepares an individual completely for all events. Each athletic event has specific needs that must be identified and included in the training program. Some positions on a team within an athletic event require training programs different from others of the same event. For example, the training program for a baseball pitcher is very different from that for an outfielder. Certain popular health club attitudes imply that specific conditioning machines or exercise programs result in total conditioning. This is not true. Following are discussions of areas we believe are important to every training program. (See also the individual chapters on nutrition, flexibility, strength training, and aerobic conditioning.)

NUTRITION

Each individual has an ideal weight at which he or she is most likely to achieve the maximum level of performance in a particular sport. This cannot be completely determined from height and weight charts but must be individualized. There is a frequent misconception that the bigger and heavier an athlete is, the stronger and better the athlete will be. This is not true. The demands of the event may determine the ideal physiology and weight of the participant.

The best way to determine your ideal weight is to learn your percentage of muscle and fat. Female athletes generally average a slightly greater body fat component than male athletes. The best-conditioned major-league baseball players have between 7% and 15% body fat. In general, those athletes who are above 20% body fat are frequently associated with undesirable slowness, lack of endurance, and performance not consistent with their ability and potential.

In general, for weight maintenance during periods of light activity, the minimum daily caloric intake is 10 times the desired weight in pounds. During moderate activity, minimum caloric intake should be 15 times the desired weight in pounds, and during heavy physical activity it should be 20 or more times the desired weight in pounds.

Some individuals try to lose weight through the use of selective medications such as diet pills or fluid pills. Both of these are to be discouraged. Most diet pills basically increase the body's metabolic system so that it works at a more rapid rate, resulting in an accelerated burning up of calories. This same end result can be accomplished by a planned diet and training program. The potential negative effect of using diet pills is that they act similarly to amphetamines or amphetamine-like substances (pep pills). They give a false sense of well-being that generally results in a depreciation of performance. Although the individual may feel better, he or she is doing worse. The use of fluid pills, or diuretics, on a regular basis may result in major changes in the water and salt composition within the body and in the function of the kidneys.

Some athletes try to get in shape by using "rubberized" sweatsuits, saunas and steambaths. However, they should understand both the benefit and the misuse of such aids. These provide a temporary weight (water) reduction process, which is frequently utilized to "make weight" for weight-determined events, for example, wrestling. But they should actively be discouraged as ongoing aids for physical conditioning. These techniques involve a water reduction, not a fat reduction, process, and in general, the water lost is returned to the system within 24–48 hours. The athlete who suddenly loses 10 pounds suddenly regains 10 pounds. If the water is not returned to the system, the individual will become dehydrated and may have other problems.

It is possible both to lose weight and remain effective and to gain weight and remain effective. However, sudden changes in weight during the sports activity period will probably affect performance and are strongly discouraged.

FLEXIBILITY

Flexibility is a key to injury prevention and smoothness of motion. Too often an athlete will work on a specific weight program during the off season only to find that certain muscle groups are tighter than before and that fluidity of motion has been lost. The athlete is stronger but not as agile as before. The degree of flexibility is determined by the looseness in the muscles, tendons and ligaments about the joints.

Whenever an individual is recovering from a musculoskeletal injury, the flexibility aspect of the training program must be carefully monitored and emphasized. All physically competitive individuals sustain micro- or mini-tears of the muscles and tendons as a result of maximum exertion. If there has been a direct, discernible muscle or tendon injury such as a hamstring pull (strain) or an Achilles tendon rupture, the flexibility concerns are paramount in comprehensive reconditioning. The micro- or mini-injuries to the shoulders and elbows of baseball pitchers are classic examples of the continued need for an off-season flexibility program.

STRENGTH AND TISSUE CONDITIONING

The need for strength and anaerobic capacity must again be individually directed according to the athlete's needs. It is necessary to consider the strength and skill requirements of the athletic activity before advising someone about a muscle and strength conditioning program. There is a definite difference between a muscle power training program and a muscle endurance conditioning program. Muscle power is the rate at which a resistance can be moved; muscle endurance is the number of repetitive muscle contractions performed in a unit of time without fatigue.

There may be some crossover in some sports between strength and skill; however, specific direction is needed to define what is appropriate for each individual and each sport. One's skill in hitting a baseball is not closely related to one's skill in bench pressing, and the strength training program should reflect such differences between sports activities.

Using weighted instruments—swinging a weighted bat in baseball, throwing a weighted ball, using a heavier tennis racquet or heavier golf clubs—must be carefully considered. To a certain extent the use of heavier equipment is a muscle endurance conditioning program and can have a positive effect in strengthening the appropriate muscles and maintaining smooth motion. On the negative side, if the objects used are too heavy, early fatigue may result. Also, the increased weight may actually involve different neuromuscular and joint reactions and could negatively affect skill development and contribute to poor biomechanical performance patterns.

Individuals working on a comprehensive training program should be concerned about tissue endurance and local tissue metabolic training. The right training programs will result in improved strength and function of bones, tendons and ligaments. These are not static tissues; they become weaker with disuse and conversely become stronger with proper use and training. A conditioning program designed to meet the physical demands of the activity or sport can improve the strength and metabolic endurance of these tissues.

AEROBIC CONDITIONING

In general, aerobic conditioning or cardiovascular endurance is the ability of the heart and lungs to supply oxygen and nutrients to exercising muscles and permit you to perform a task for progressively longer periods of time. It makes the difference in being able to maintain maximum output for all of a particular event for the entire season. Our chapter on aerobic conditioning focuses on this aspect of the training program. The development of skills appropriate to the sport requires that the aerobic conditioning techniques be sports-specific, addressing the needs of a baseball player as distinct from the golfer and the triathlon competitor. Each individual should seek appropriate advice from a health professional in determining the guidelines for his or her aerobic conditioning program.

In working out a training program it is important to consider long-distance running both for the overall strengthening of muscles and for the secondary effect it has on developing improved muscular endurance and anaerobic conditioning. To achieve maximum conditioning one should plan both long-distance running and wind sprints. Running stadium steps is a good combination exercise, as it develops leg strength as well as endurance. Bicycle riding and swimming may be considered as other alternatives for developing endurance. Swimming provides excellent arm conditioning and shoulder flexibility. However, bicycle riding and swimming probably contribute less to lower-leg bone, tendon and ligament conditioning.

SPEED

It is possible to improve one's speed through good conditioning techniques as well as through improved techniques of running. Speed is also important in moving into position on the field or court. The speed of hand-eye coordination can be sharpened through practice and development. It may be improved through practice in one's sport or through any other form of racquet sport (i.e., racquetball, squash and tennis). Some individuals feel that even by playing electronic games you may develop a basic sense of reaction time. This is the opportunity to activate eye-brain-hand coordination. Hand-foot reaction time can be improved through practice. All of these speed factors should be considered as integral in your training program.

STRESS

Stress is a factor in all aspects of sports and life. When there has been a flaw in an athlete's performance, it is important that he or she has a system to deal with the ensuing stress—was the mistake failure or an unfortunate event? The response to such stress is, in part, a reflection of the attitudes encouraged by parents and coaches. Those individuals who have received positive feedback will recover more positively and more quickly than those who have been punished by negative attitudes and negative discipline and have developed a fear of failure. The athlete who is encouraged to perform at his or her maximum ability is usually able to resume the program with less stressful carry-over. The athlete who fears failure is much slower to respond. Part of the athlete's self-image and attitude is born within; however, a positive attitude on the part of the family and coach will greatly facilitate the ability of an athlete to cope with stress and discouragement. Mental strategies, including ways to deal with stress, are an important part of a comprehensive training program. These are discussed in detail in chapter 5.

SPECIFIC TRAINING PROGRAMS

Your training program must be planned on a long-range model, with specific objectives for different times of the year. The competitive level of performance does not matter; a planned training program will result in better physical and psychological conditioning and better preparation for your individual or team performance. A general annual training approach to a team sport, baseball, is described here.

Professional baseball requires year-round concerns for physical conditioning and good health. We consider the baseball year in four periods:

Immediate postseason	October–January
Preparatory preseason	January–March
Spring training	March
Competitive season	April–October

Immediate postseason. This period should be used to identify and resolve physical problems. If the athlete plans to initiate or change a strength or weight training program, it should be done during this period so the body can adjust to its new form and functions prior to the competitive season. General conditioning should start after a brief rest period at the end of the season.

Preparatory preseason. This period should be used to fine-tune general conditioning and improve specific skills. This is the major physical training period for improving strength, flexibility and endurance. In addition, the athlete should increase his or her throwing, batting and speed drills.

Spring training. At the onset of spring training, weight should be near desired playing weight and the athlete should be in top physical condition. Concern should be directed to a maintenance conditioning program and to the improvement and sharpening of baseball skills.

Competitive season. Conditioning goals during the season involve maintenance—avoid major weight changes and deconditioning. Train on a regularly scheduled basis, preferably three times a week. Training with a partner is helpful. For training to be beneficial, it must be done on a consistent basis and be of sufficient intensity and duration.

INJURY AND TRAINING

Whenever a person is recovering from an injury, many other parts of the body that remain uninjured and can be used to continue a moderate to vigorous continued conditioning program. This requires outlining two separate programs—the treatment and rehabilitation program for the injured part and a continued modified training program for the remainder of the body—and then integrating the two separate programs.

The importance of maintaining fitness in the injured athlete, especially the professional athlete, is seen in the case of a major-league baseball player who suffered a groin pull. Carl Yastrzemski was pursuing the 3,000th hit of his glorious career with the Boston Red Sox when he sustained a left-sided groin pull (partial tear of the adductor longus tendon). He was initially treated with ice packs for 20 minutes every 2 hours for 36 hours and alternating treatment with a portable TENS (transcutaneous electric nerve stimulator) unit for 20 minutes every 2 hours for relief of acute pain and thus minimization of secondary spasm. When the local sensitivity had subsided he was started on active assisted exercises for maintenance of range of motion. Along with this exercise program for his recent injury, he continued on a stationary bicycle for aerobic training and weight conditioning for his upper body and legs. After seven days he was able to return to gentle hitting practice and slow jogging. While his injury treatment progressed he maintained his general conditioning program and was able to return to the lineup when his fourteen-day disability was over.

A comprehensive training program must include an analysis of behavioral and physical aspects of lifestyle and fitness, a coordinated program to promote and enhance an improved understanding of behavioral health and fitness habits, and an individually developed health prescription that defines a program to achieve your objectives.

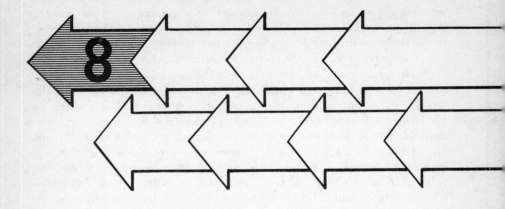

I think it is an immutable law in business that words are words, explanations are explanations, promises are promises—but only performance is reality. Performance alone is the best measure of your confidence, competence and courage. Only performance gives you the freedom to grow as yourself.

Harold Geneen, Chairman Emeritus, ITT

This is where we put it all together.

Each of us strives to be the best we can be and each of us has known the special feeling of satisfaction of working toward a difficult goal and summoning our best effort. None of us can hope to live continuously in the bright light of peak performance, but we can live the kind of life, adopt the habits and cultivate the attitudes that allow us to make the most of our abilities.

In this chapter, we will look at some of the themes common to all great performances. The lessons are universal. Great performances are seldom isolated events. Usually they result from years of dedication, hard

PERFORMANCE

work, goal setting and perseverance. We believe that conscientious effort in the areas outlined in the 7 Building Blocks will not only help you lead a healthier and more fit life, but also help you achieve your best performance.

HEALTH, FITNESS AND PERFORMANCE: THE LINKAGES

The concept that health and fitness are linked to an individual's ability to perform is not new. The belief that a sound mind and sound body are inseparable dates back to the ancient Greeks. Recent surveys have linked improved fitness to more energy, less perceived stress, more job satisfaction and even an improved sex life! Here are some of the more important factors that lead to the best of performances:

Setting Goals

Most great performers have learned how to set goals—both short-term and long-term—in order to achieve success. This applies not just to top athletes, but also to individuals who are top achievers in other walks of life. One woman we know was recently honored as one of the top salespeople for a large computer company. Her greatest successes came in the first several years after the birth of her first child. She described her success as follows:

> Having a child helped me organize my priorities. I no longer had a lot of free time so I had to plan accordingly. I never go into work anymore without a concept of what I need to accomplish that day. I make it a point to tackle the hardest challenges first, and not leave them for another day.

Several aspects of goal setting seem particularly important. First, *the goals must be realistic*. In weight loss, for example, it's not a realistic goal to lose 10 pounds in a week. We would rather see an individual plan to lose a pound a week for 10 weeks—a more reasonable goal, and more likely to be successful ultimately. Second, it is important to develop a *specific plan*. Again, in the area of weight loss it's important for the individual to write down a plan for how that pound-a-week loss is going to occur. In the area of aerobic exercise, plans are also important. That's why virtually every top runner keeps a training logbook. It helps you chart your progress and develop a specific program. That's why we have given you specific 20-week exercise prescriptions to help get you started on this planning process. Finally, it's very important to establish a *reward*. Perhaps the personal satisfaction you receive from sticking to your plan will be sufficient. But we would also encourage you to establish a specific reward. Buy yourself a new bathing suit after you have lost 10 pounds, or a new pair of running shoes after you have completed the first 20 weeks of a running program. Take your family out to dinner with the money you have saved by stopping cigarette smoking. Such rewards are a way of recognizing your achievement, and they give you something to look forward to.

Consistency

All great athletes know that the key to a successful career is consistency. The monumental achievements of Pete Rose breaking Ty Cobb's career hit mark, Kareem Abdul-Jabbar establishing the NBA career scoring record or Tom Seaver winning 300 games are all based on consistent performance year in and year out.

How does one establish consistency? There's not one simple answer. In part it has to do with having an overall sense of what you want to achieve and a specific plan for implementation. Even more important are concentration and attention to detail. John McEnroe has said that he always practices as if he were playing a match. Bjorn Borg was famous for his four- and five-hour workouts. The poet T. S. Eliot wrote every morning until noon. When someone asked him, "Don't you find that painful?" he responded, "It would be far more painful not to write."

Different patterns work for different people, and we encourage you to find the patterns that work for you. To achieve the important benefits you will need to establish patterns and habits that result in consistency.

Sense of Mission

By a sense of mission we mean the ability to perceive a larger cause for your actions. Some individuals are driven by religious beliefs, others by a desire to provide a better life for their families. Still others derive great joy from the personal satisfaction that they have given their absolute best effort. A sense of mission often allows individuals to achieve efforts not even they thought were possible. The early space engineers and astronauts were caught up in the intense effort to conquer space, and their intensity often produced results that startled them as well as bystanders. A sense of mission allows an individual to maintain a long-term perspective and keep goals in sight despite momentary ups and downs.

Positive Attitudes

High achievers typically display a variety of positive attitudes. One theme that continually emerges is responsibility. The top performers do not make excuses; rather, they accept responsibility both for successes and failures. This may take the form of getting out of bed to go to the hospital for a sick patient or staying late to finish a report that others are counting on for the next day.

A central component to a lifelong health and fitness program is the understanding that *you* carry the major responsibility for these important matters in your life. Fortunately, more and more individuals have begun to recognize the significance that their own actions and habits have for their overall health.

Teamwork and Cooperation

In our conversations with high performers in business and sports we have been struck by the importance they place on teamwork and cooperation. A number of athletic teams have been characterized by a high level of teamwork. Perhaps none epitomized this more than the New York Knickerbockers basketball teams in the late 1960s and early 1970s. The starting team was characterized by five players who worked so well together that they seemed to be able to anticipate each other's moves all the time. Their heightened sense of teamwork made them a formidable team and carried them to an NBA championship. Successful business leaders also recognize the importance of teamwork to accomplish large objectives that no individual could achieve alone.

Close Interpersonal Relationships

When we surveyed one group of highly successful business people prior to a presentation, over 80%, listed their spouse or family as the source of greatest satisfaction in their lives. This has also been true of the vast majority of professional athletes with whom we have worked. High-level performance can exact a heavy price in terms of emotional and physical stress. Loving and supportive relationships with family and friends can be crucial to keep things in perspective.

Sports Performance

We are a nation that loves sports. Over half of the adult population in the United States reports regular involvement with exercise and sports and less than 5% claims that sports do not matter to them.

In the past twenty years, major scientific advances have occurred in virtually every aspect of sports performance. New information in areas ranging from mental preparation and training regimens to equipment and playing surfaces have revolutionized modern sports and led to an unprecedented assault on the record books. These advances also have enabled more people to be involved in sports, enhanced the pleasure of the recreational athlete and increased the safety of competition. Some of the new frontiers in sports performance research include the following:

Mental Training

There is intense interest among athletes on mind/body interaction. The higher the level of competition, the more intense the interest. Once you reach the level of professional or Olympic athletes, the differences in physical ability are very small, and even the slightest mental edge can assume disproportionate importance.

Mental training is not a panacea. But techniques such as relaxation, visualization and mindfulness training are being applied more and more to sports. And we're going to see a lot more of this in years to come, as we continue to explore the interface between mind and body (see chapter 5).

Physical Training

The area of physical training and its relation to sports performance is also of intense research interest. We've spoken about some of the advances in the field in the chapters on aerobic capacity and training. While we have learned a great deal, we have only scratched the surface of understanding the optimum training programs for sports performance.

Many people credit the recent successes of East German Olympic teams to programs that identify potential early and then blend science into every phase of training. Unfortunately, the United States has lagged behind in this domain. Despite the efforts of many talented exercise scientists, there still is some reluctance to apply the knowledge available to training our athletes.

Avoiding Injury

It used to be thought that injuries were an inevitable part of athletic competition. Indeed, a certain number of injuries are probably unavoidable as individuals strain to extract the ultimate performance from their bodies. However, we now also know that thoughtful training programs to strengthen muscles and improve flexibility, proper warm-up and so on, combined with the best equipment available, can dramatically reduce the incidence of injuries in sports. Injury reduction provides an excellent example of how medicine can enhance sports performance.

Sports Equipment

In our lifetime we have seen a revolution in equipment, all the way from skis and tennis racquets to running and walking shoes. The poles used by pole vaulters provide a classic example: Vaulters have moved from bamboo, to metal, to fiberglass, to combinations of fiberglass and graphite. The interaction between sport and science is probably nowhere more evident than in the area of equipment design.

CONTROVERSIES IN SPORTS PERFORMANCE

Cocaine Abuse

One of the biggest problems in sports in recent history is the problem of drug abuse. In the past few years a growing number of reports have raised the alarm about cocaine use in American professional sports. No one knows for sure the exact extent of the problem—but early indications suggest that it is a major one.

The link between cocaine use and efforts to enhance performance is not immediately apparent. Yet we believe that a subtle connection exists. Professional sports in the United States is a big business. Athletes are often paid large sums of money based on their performance and are subject to intense pressure. Professional athletes are, in short, in a position to be very susceptible to cocaine abuse. First, they have the money to afford this very expensive addiction. Second, they may fall prey to the illusion that cocaine will enhance their performance or at least give them a temporary escape from the heavy pressures of daily performance.

As physicians we feel it is important to set the record straight about cocaine. First, there is no convincing evidence that it enhances athletic performance. On the contrary, there is very compelling evidence that cocaine use *detracts* from performance. Indeed, one of the great tragedies is that it has already destroyed the careers of a number of fine young professional athletes. Second, some people maintain that cocaine is not addictive. This is simply not true. It is a highly addictive drug from both a physical and a psychological standpoint. We can only add our voices to the many other concerned physicians who have condemned cocaine use among athletes in the strongest possible terms.

We should also point out that cocaine addiction is a disease, and as in any other drug addiction, individuals with this disease need prompt and effective treatment.

Anabolic Steroid Abuse

Perhaps even more alarming than the abuse of cocaine is the use of anabolic steroids. There is mounting evidence that these substances may be in fairly wide use among athletes who are involved in strength training. Nobody knows for certain exactly how widespread the use of anabolic steroids has become. Several studies in the 1970s suggested that 60–70% of world-class shot putters, javelin throwers or discus throwers were currently on or had at some point experimented with anabolic steroids. Recent articles have suggested that the use of these agents may be fairly prevalent among interior linemen in professional football and may have permeated into college and even high school football programs. There are also some disconcerting reports of increased anabolic steroid use among women in sports.

The anabolic steroids are similar to male sex hormones. The normal physiologic role of male sex hormones, androgens, is to promote the development of male sexual characteristics as well as growth of bones and muscle mass. Those athletes who have taken anabolic steroids have done this with the hope of increasing their muscle mass and strength.

There is no convincing evidence that taking anabolic steroids increases strength. There are some isolated reports of individuals gaining significant amounts of weight while taking them. But we do not know if this extra weight represents fat, water, muscle or some combination of the three. One of the very great difficulties in attempting to study the effects of anabolic steroids is that individuals take very different doses, with some athletes taking up to ten times the dosage that might be prescribed to treat a hormonal deficiency.

The major reason for our concern about athletes taking anabolic steroids lies in the possible medical side effects. Anabolic steroid consumption has been associated with premature closure of the growth plates in bones, atrophy of the testicles and some forms of liver cancer.

When we presented these facts to one young bodybuilder at a world championship where we were performing medical tests, he responded that he didn't care about these issues, and he refused to go into a competition in which he would not be taking anabolic steroids and the other competitors would. This is clearly a case of a misplaced sense of perspective. Young athletes are particularly susceptible to try things that might give them a competitive advantage. Often in this quest they may be tempted to experiment with substances like anabolic steroids. In these cases athletes need protection. Physicians, coaches and trainers need to speak out strongly and categorically against the use of anabolic steroids.

Blood Doping

In the spring of 1985 some very alarming reports surfaced about members of the United States Olympic cycling team engaging in the process of "blood doping" during the 1984 Olympics. Blood doping is a technique in which the athlete receives a transfusion of red blood cells prior to a competition. The red blood cells can be from the athlete himself or herself (in which case they have been previously removed and stored) or from someone with a compatible blood type. It is alleged that this practice is common among Eastern European cyclists.

Whether or not blood doping enhances performance remains very controversial. There is no scientific evidence we are aware of that shows any clear-cut benefit. We were very concerned about the report of blood doping in the American cyclists for a number of reasons. First, there are a number of complications possible with blood transfusions. There is a small but definite risk of hepatitis. Even with careful cross-matching there is a small risk of transfusion reactions. For these reasons we try to minimize transfusions in hospitalized patients. Second, even if blood doping is not technically against rules which do not allow the use of drugs to enhance performance, we believe that it violates the spirit of these regulations. Third, it appears that the blood doping occurred with the approval of some of the coaches and physicians associated with the team. We feel that young athletes, who are still formulating their views of the world, should be *protected* by coaches and physicians, not encouraged to adopt questionable and maybe even dangerous practices.

EXPLORING THE BOUNDARIES OF SPORTS PERFORMANCE

In many ways, this whole book is about boundaries. In the 7 Building Blocks, we have shared with you new scientific information which influences both health and fitness. We are convinced that a systematic use of our 7 Building Blocks system will improve both your health and fitness and also improve your day-to-day and lifelong performance. Does this mean that we're going to turn your tennis game into one that will challenge John McEnroe or give you the perfect explanation for why Larry Bird is such a great basketball player? Of course not.

While we have much new knowledge at our disposal, we have only scratched the surface of explaining human performance. Even if we could explain the physiology and biomechanics of a great athlete, this explanation would fall far short of a total understanding. For in the end there is that amazing force of the human will and spirit which makes each of us unique and drives us toward our goals and our own maximum performance.

9

Pain and Performance

In athletics, pain may be a warning signal that advises an individual not to participate for fear of further injury. Some athletes seek medical help. Others may participate in sports despite pain. Those with high levels of tolerance are able to withstand greater discomfort and continue with their activity, whereas those with lower pain tolerance levels are more likely to interrupt their activities. Some of these levels of pain tolerance may be genetic, whereas some are affected by social and cultural factors, or by the contest itself. In competition only the experienced sports health professional staff is able to determine the risks involved for an athlete who continues to compete with pain.

There are very few successful high-performance athletes who do *not* frequently compete when they are in pain. If an individual feels a pain and does not believe that he or she can continue, that person should not be advised otherwise. No one should ever try to mask the pain of an athlete and encourage the athlete to continue participation. For example, the injection of a local anesthetic into a sprained ankle will decrease the sensitivity of the protective mechanism of pain and make the individual feel better and more comfortable. The internal mechanism that advises that person to protect himself or herself against further injury has been deadened, however, and a second injury to the affected area will result in a much more severe injury, possibly a career-ending one. It should be emphasized that pain-altering medications and injections should never be used to permit an athlete to continue participation when it may endanger an athlete's performance or future.

An individual may have pain that will not be affected by participation, and in such an instance the use of local anesthetic infiltration may be permissible. An example is the athlete who has an abscessed tooth or, as in a recent World Series, the baseball player who has a thrombosed hemorrhoid.

INTERPRETATION AND TREATMENT OF PAIN

The interpretation and treatment of pain presents a major challenge for the sports health professional. Pain is a part of any intense participation in sport. Frequently the immediate assessment and treatment of pain will determine whether an individual should continue to participate.

There are four general categories to be considered when treating pain associated with sports: physical measures, medications, physical rehabilitation and psychosocial factors.

PHYSICAL MEASURES

The physical measures available for the treatment of acute and chronic pain resulting from athletic participation include the following:

- external supports
- cold and hot therapy
- massage and manipulation
- penetrating therapy
- surgical intervention

External supports used in the treatment of acute pain may include splints, casts or other assistive devices. For example, any injury to an extremity or to the spine in which a fracture is suspected should be immobilized before transporting the injured athlete.

An orthosis or orthotic device is any assistive device that protects or stabilizes. All braces and other external supportive devices are orthotics. However, in athletic terminology the word *orthotic* usually refers to a supplemental footwear device designed to correct an abnormality or deficiency. Such orthotics may be built into the shoe or made for insertion into the shoe.

Cold and hot therapy are frequently used for the treatment of acute as well as chronic pain. In the treatment of acute pain, cold therapy (cryotherapy) is important. The use of cold provides two immediate effects; the constriction of local blood vessels to minimize swelling, and a local numbing or pain relieving. A spray coolant such as ethyl chloride or chloral methane provides immediate cooling and local pain relief in the injured area. In some instances, this relief is enough to let a participant continue in a sports activity. Cryotherapy, in addition to effecting local pain relief, may have some psychological value. Cold application should be applied for a minimum of 20 minutes. Stroking the area with a piece of ice may bring relief.

The use of heat for the treatment of chronic pain and during rehabilitation after injury is very commonplace. Heat should not be used immediately after an acute injury. The use of heat for pain relief increases circulation, which helps decrease swelling and ease muscle and joint mobility. The most common method for direct application of heat to an area is the use of moist, warm packs. The other frequently used method for applying heat is a whirlpool bath.

Massage or the manipulation of soft tissues is an important method for treatment for pain. The stroking of and pressure to an area encourage circulation and decompression of accumulated tissue fluids from that area. Also, it is possible to stretch soft tissues with some local scar tissue from a previous injury. There are secondary effects of massage that are relaxing to the rest of the body. The types of massage most frequently used in athletics are the stroking massage (effleurage) or a deep kneading massage (pétrissage).

Penetrating therapies or so-called "thermodynamic modalities" must be carefully performed and monitored by personnel who are trained in their theory and use. These methods are never implemented in the treatment of acute pain; they are for recurring or chronic pain. The four most common penetrating therapies are diathermy, ultrasound, direct muscle stimulation and transelectrical nerve stimulation (TENS).

When all of the other physical measures are not effective, patients must consider surgical intervention to correct the problem. Or they may need to think about changing their sport or the position they play.

MEDICATIONS

It is often necessary to use medications for the relief of acute or chronic pain. The three categories of medications most frequently used are pain relievers, anti-inflammatory agents and muscle relaxants.

Pain Relievers

Exactly which medication is selected for pain relief usually depends on the severity of the pain. Pain relief medication for acute pain may be mild enough to let an athlete continue or strong enough to provide relief from severe pain, such as an open fracture. When determining how to treat pain, it is important that sports health professionals realize that pain is subjective. It is also important for sports health professionals to recognize the need to alleviate pain as soon as possible. One must be particularly careful about using pain-alleviating medications on a continuing basis because other factors—particularly drug tolerance and physical dependence—may become of greater significance.

The group of medications most frequently considered in the treatment of pain are non-narcotic analgesics such as acetylsalicylic acid (aspirin) and acetaminophen (the principal ingredient in Tylenol). Among the milder prescriptive pain-relieving medications are propoxyphene hydrochloride (Darvon) and combinations of analgesics with codeine. It should be noted that at one time Darvon was considered to be potentially less habit-forming than codeine and was therefore used more frequently for the treatment of chronic pain. This has become a greater concern as many people reportedly have become dependent on this pain medication. If stronger medications are needed, narcotic analgesics should be considered. In the past morphine was considered the strongest of these medications. Other frequently used narcotic analgesics include meperidine (used in Demerol), oxycodone hydrochloride (used in Percodan) and codeine. If you were selecting an oral medication for moderate to severe pain, you would be likely to select either codeine mixed with a non-narcotic analgesic or Percodan. If you were selecting an injectable pain-relieving medication, you would more likely select either Demerol or morphine. In some instances, it may be advisable to inject a local anesthetic, such as lidocaine hydrochloride (Xylocaine) or bupivacaine hydrochloride (Sensorcaine). If an athlete has an acutely sensitive tendinitis or bursitis, the use of injectable local anesthetics with anti-inflammatory agents (cortisone, for example) provides pain relief and an associated anti-inflammatory effect. Again, it is important to emphasize that except in the most unusual circumstances narcotic analgesics should *not* be used for individuals with chronic pain. Injectable local anesthetics may be used in specific instances as peripheral nerve blocks or regional anesthetics but not routinely in the treatment of chronic pain syndromes.

Anti-Inflammatory Agents

Anti-inflammatory medications are commonly used in the treatment of recurrent acute or chronic pain that is secondary to inflammation. In general the anti-inflammatory medications are divided into two categories: nonsteroidal anti-inflammatory drugs (NSAIDs) and glucocorticoids, or steroidal anti-inflammatory agents. The oldest and most popular, and also very effective, nonsteroidal anti-inflammatory agent is aspirin. Other frequently used NSAIDs include ibuprofen (Motrin, Rufen, Advil), naproxen (Naprosyn), indomethacin (Indocin, including a sustained release form), sulindac (Clinoril), and phenylbutazone (Butazolidin).

All the aforementioned nonsteroidal anti-inflammatory agents are effective in suppressing inflammation, in addition to providing an analgesic effect. It must be cautioned that whenever these substances are used, virtually all of them have significant side effects not necessarily duplicated by other nonsteroidal anti-inflammatory agents. For example, if someone develops headaches or nausea from one medication, it does not necessarily indicate that he or she will have the same reactions to another of the NSAIDs. Also, some individuals may not experience relief from one of the nonsteroidal anti-inflammatory agents yet may experience significant relief from another.

The most frequently discussed anti-inflammatory agent is cortisone or hydrocortisone. This medication has a very major inflammation suppression effect. Therefore its use as an anti-inflammatory medication will provide dramatic relief from the common athletic inflammatory problems of tendinitis and bursitis. However, there are significant long-term side effects from the repeated use of cortisone, such as salt retention, fluid retention, bone resorption and other potential generalized problems. Most physicians do not recommend the use of cortisone on a long-term or frequent basis.

Muscle Relaxants

The third group of drugs frequently used for acute and chronic pain are muscle relaxants. Those seem to have a combination of possible effects: They decrease muscle spasm, provide an analgesic effect and mild sedative action and relieve anxiety. Some of the drugs frequently used, alone or in combination with other pain-relieving medications, include cyclobenzaprine hydrochloride (Flexeril), carisoprodol (Soma), orphenadrine citrate (Norflex), methocarbamol (Robaxin), and diazepam (Valium). The use of any of these drugs must be carefully monitored as to the possible effects. Using other medications and particularly alcohol with muscle relaxants may have serious and hazardous effects.

PHYSICAL REHABILITATION

Without proper rehabilitation, injured athletes may recover from an injury only to hurt themselves again. Therefore it is critical to treat the pain and to appreciate other problems caused by it. Medications may ease the pain and decrease the inflammation but may not resolve the secondary problems. A careful and specific program must be formed as part of the treatment of pain.

PSYCHOSOCIAL FACTORS

The psychosocial aspects of pain should not be forgotten. At times it is very difficult to determine whether a chronic pain problem is the result of injury or low pain tolerance, or whether it is a way of coping for an athlete who no longer desires to participate and is seeking a face-saving exit. Pain is a frequent and gracious way for many adolescents to withdraw from competition without appearing to have failed.

CLASSIFICATION OF PAIN

The current system for the classification of pain consists of six categories:

- acute pain
- subacute pain
- recurrent acute pain
- ongoing acute pain
- chronic benign pain
- chronic intractable benign pain syndrome

Acute pain. Acute pain lasts from minutes to days and may vary in intensity from mild to severe. The definitions for mild, moderate and severe pain are obviously subjective and reflect the health care professional's interpretation of the injured person's reaction.

Subacute pain. Subacute pain is usually days to weeks in duration and mild to moderate in intensity. In the early phases of subacute pain, it is considered to be primarily a peripheral pain; however, if it extends for many weeks, there may be a central nervous system contribution to the pain. Subacute pain is generally not associated with a medical emergency and treatment may require the use of mild oral analgesics.

Recurrent acute pain. Recurrent acute pain is intermittent in nature and usually lasts only a few days. In most instances there is some underlying chronic pathological process. The intensity of the pain is mild to moderate and is primarily of local or peripheral origin. Most examples of recurrent acute pain in athletes are associated with the so-called "overuse syndrome." This term implies that an athlete is doing more than his or her body is conditioned to do or more than the local tissues are prepared to respond to without injury.

Ongoing acute pain. The pain may last for weeks and does possess some chronic characteristics. The intensity may be from mild to moderate. The treatment includes pain-relieving medications ranging from analgesics to orally administered analgesic/mild narcotic drugs. There should not be any need for injectable medications.

Chronic benign pain. Chronic benign pain usually lasts from weeks to months. The severity of the pain is minimal to moderate. The pain is primarily of central (spinal and brain) origin. In general, this type of pain requires multispecialty evaluation and treatment. This is one of the most difficult pain problems to identify and treat successfully in athletics. We may identify an athlete who continues to complain of shoulder pain, knee pain or back pain with minimal or negative physical, laboratory and radiographic findings. A complaint of pain or a questionable injury may reflect a reluctance to participate.

Chronic intractable benign pain syndrome. This syndrome usually lasts longer than six months and is manifested by pain of intensity ranging from mild to severe. The pain becomes the primary focal point of the individual's existence. Pain may be localized about a specific anatomical region, frequently a shoulder or knee, and at times becomes so severe and untreatable that it alters an athlete's entire life and outlook on life. Although the pain is perceived at a peripheral level, the psychological features of the pain become so overwhelming that the term *psychosomatic* may be applicable. The treatment is definitely nonsurgical and must be multidisciplinary, with a major psychotherapeutic involvement. If there is atrophy and abnormal function in a specific region, a continued physical rehabilitation regimen should be included.

In this discussion of pain, there are guidelines about the experiences likely to be encountered in treating athletes with pain. The easiest pain to treat is that of acute injury. The more recurrent and chronic the pain, the more complex the evaluation and the ultimate treatment of the pain. With competitive individuals, the need or desire to withdraw from competition is always a reality. Injury and pain are the most frequent and the most unembarrassing way to withdraw from competition. It is important that we recognize these points and realize that all of our surgical and rehabilitative skills will probably not overcome that particular personal need of the athlete.

10

Risk Factor Reduction and Positive Lifestyle

Cardiovascular diseases result in over half the deaths in adults each year in the United States. Coronary artery disease (CAD), the process underlying angina and heart attack, is by far the largest single killer in our society. These grim facts become all the more unfortunate when we realize that many cases of CAD would be prevented if individuals lived healthier lives and reduced their risk factors.

More and more individuals have come to recognize the importance of controlling risk factors. While this is very encouraging, we should not become overconfident. Over 25% of our population still smokes cigarettes. At least 25% of individuals with high blood pressure are not adequately treated. The average American eats *double* the amount of cholesterol each day that the American Heart Association recommends. While we have come a long way, there is still a long way to go.

WHAT ARE RISK FACTORS?

Simply stated, risk factors are aspects of your lifestyle and habits or your physical condition that influence the chances that you will develop coronary artery disease. Considerable research sponsored by the National Institutes of Health, the American Heart Association and other concerned organizations has helped clarify exactly what these risk factors are. One of the most important of these studies has been conducted in the community of Framingham, Massachusetts, where over 5,000 adults have been followed for over twenty-five years to see which habits and conditions are linked to an increase in CAD. The established risk factors are outlined in the table below.

Risk Factors for Developing Coronary Artery Disease	
Major Risk Factors	Minor Risk Factors
1. Hypertension 2. Elevated cholesterol 3. Cigarette smoking	1. Obesity 2. Sedentary lifestyle 3. Diabetes and glucose intolerance 4. Positive family history 5. Type A personality

A quick perusal of this table shows that most of these risk factors are entirely under your control. The major risk factors are the ones which are particularly important to control since each of these has been clearly linked to increased CAD. It is also important to understand that the risk factors multiply each other rather than add to each other. As shown in fig. 43, if you have one major risk factor your chances of developing CAD are doubled. If you have two major risk factors your chances are *quadrupled* and if you have all three major risk factors your chances of developing coronary artery disease are increased *eightfold!*

MAJOR RISK FACTORS

Hypertension

Hypertension, or high blood pressure, afflicts 35 million people. It is the most significant risk factor for both heart attack and stroke. Over 90% of individuals who suffer stroke have a history of hypertension. High blood pressure has been called "the silent killer" because it usually presents no symptoms. Unfortunately, in the vast majority of individuals, we still do not know the exact cause of high blood pressure. Less than 5% of individuals with high blood pressure have a definable medical cause. The other approximately 95% have what we call "essential" hypertension, where no definite underlying cause can be found.

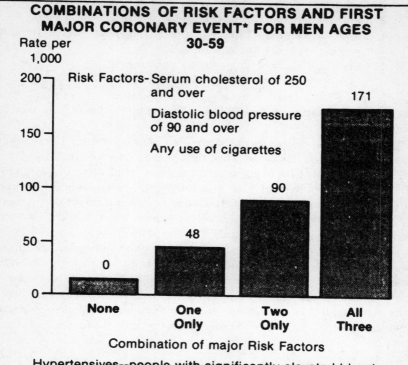

COMBINATIONS OF RISK FACTORS AND FIRST MAJOR CORONARY EVENT* FOR MEN AGES 30-59

Rate per 1,000

Risk Factors- Serum cholesterol of 250 and over

Diastolic blood pressure of 90 and over

Any use of cigarettes

None	One Only	Two Only	All Three
0	48	90	171

Combination of major Risk Factors

Hypertensives--people with significantly elevated blood pressure are four times more prone to stroke than people with normal blood pressure; diabetic hypersensitive, six times. People with normal blood pressure seldom get strokes.

Graph illustrates the increased risk of a coronary event* with the presence of one or more risk factors. For example, with no risk factors present, the rate is 20 events per 1,000 people, while with the three risk factors present the rate is 171 events per 1,000 people.

* A coronary event is defined as any clinically significant manifestation of coronary artery disease, such as heart attack or angina.

There is more and more evidence that increased salt in our daily diet plays a role in hypertension. The average American eats between 10 and 15 grams of salt a day. This is many times what we *need* in our diet. Much of this (probably two-thirds) comes from processed foods, while the remainder comes from adding salt in cooking and at the table.

There are a number of commonsense guidelines to control salt in the average American diet. We typically emphasize the following points:

1. Emphasize fresh fruits and vegetables in your diet.
2. Limit the amount of snack foods in your diet.
3. Limit the number of times you eat at fast-food restaurants; fast foods are typically *loaded* with salt.
4. Check the labels on foods for sodium content.

In the case of infants, most baby-food manufacturers have already cut back on the amount of sodium. It is very important *not* to salt baby food to *your* taste.

Of major importance is *detecting* high blood pressure. Every adult should have his or her blood pressure checked on a yearly basis. Over 70% of individuals with hypertension have the "mild" form of the condition. For these individuals, we generally recommend weight loss, salt restriction and sometimes stress reduction before resorting to drug therapy. Individuals with moderate or severe hypertension should be started on drug therapy under a physician's supervision.

Regular aerobic exercise has been shown to be an important component of sustained weight loss, and weight loss is in turn strongly linked to decreased blood pressure. Therefore, aerobic exercise may play an important indirect role on blood pressure control. We discourage individuals with high blood pressure from performing resistance strength training exercises until their blood pressure is brought under control.

Elevated Cholesterol

Elevated blood cholesterol is the second major risk factor for developing coronary artery disease. Cholesterol is a naturally occurring, waxy substance with a number of essential biological functions. It is needed to produce certain hormones and plays an essential role in cell structure. When too much cholesterol is present in the bloodstream it has a tendency to be deposited on the inner walls of arteries, forming a fatty plaque.

Cholesterol is both manufactured by the body and obtained from foods. The vast majority of Americans with elevated cholesterol have this condition from increased dietary intake.

Many studies have linked elevated cholesterol and coronary artery disease. The Framingham Study clearly showed this association. The recently completed Lipid Research Clinic Trial sponsored by the National Heart, Lung and Blood Institute, demonstrated that aggressive treatment of elevated cholesterol significantly decreases the likelihood of heart attack.

What should the average person do about cholesterol? First of all, every adult should know his or her cholesterol level. This involves a simple blood test. Make sure your doctor obtains a cholesterol level at your next visit *and* tells you the result. Since we know that cholesterol levels tend to rise with age, this test should be repeated periodically—at least once every five years over the age of 40.

It makes sense to monitor the amount of cholesterol in your diet. The American Heart Association recommends that the general public consume a diet with no more than 30% of total calories as fat, 55% as carbohydrate and 15% as protein. Cholesterol intake should be limited to less than 300 milligrams per day. The average American consumes 500 to 600 milligrams of cholesterol a day—almost twice the amount recommended by the American Heart Association! Over 50% of middle-aged Americans have cholesterol levels above 200 milligrams per deciliter—above the ideal of 130 to 190 milligrams per deciliter established by the AHA and in the range where the risk of coronary heart disease rapidly increases.

It is important to cut down the amount of eggs, dairy products and red meat in your diet. A program of strict weight control will also help lower cholesterol levels. Individuals who adopt these guidelines will typically experience a 10–15% reduction in their blood cholesterol—a very significant improvement for the average American.

Cigarette Smoking

Cigarette smoking is the number-one preventable cause of death in our society. Every year cigarette smoking is estimated to be responsible for over 300,000 premature deaths in the United States. Most people are aware of the connection between cigarette smoking and lung cancer, and indeed there is a very strong correlation. Amazingly, many people are unaware of the connection between cigarette smoking and heart disease. Of all the smoking-related deaths each year, one in five is related to lung cancer whereas one in three is related to heart disease. If you smoke more than a pack of cigarettes a day, your chances of suffering a heart attack are three times as great as those for a nonsmoker.

Why are cigarettes bad for your heart? Two of the products of cigarettes and cigarette smoke—nicotine and carbon monoxide—have been implicated in developing coronary artery disease.

Nicotine is a mild stimulant. It causes the heart rate to rise and results in increased blood pressure, and it lowers the heart's threshold to rhythm disturbances. It may also play a direct role in stimulating atherosclerosis by increasing free fatty acids in the blood and increasing the stickiness of platelets—the blood's main clotting elements.

Carbon monoxide can starve the heart and body tissues for oxygen. The federal government strictly regulates the amount of carbon monoxide levels in industrial environments. Heavy cigarette smokers regularly subject themselves to *eight times* the amount of carbon monoxide the federal government allows in industry.

Minor Risk Factors

Obesity

It has been estimated that over half the adult population in the United States is overweight. Obesity is associated with elevated cholesterol, hypertension and glucose intolerance, and because of these associations it must be considered to contribute to the risk of coronary artery disease. The good news is that weight loss is associated with an improvement in all of these associated risk factors.

Obesity is hard on virtually every organ system. Extra weight is hard on bones and joints. Lung function is often abnormal in severe obesity. A variety of endocrinologic disturbances occur, including oversecretion of insulin, abnormal menstrual cycles and changes in the levels of a variety of hormones in the bloodstream. Obese individuals are also subject to a variety of prejudices in our society which may hinder social adjustment and economic advancement.

In most instances obesity results from overeating or physical inactivity or a combination of the two. Perhaps the most important treatment for obesity is prevention. During childhood and adolescence the number of fat cells (adipocytes) can grow. Obese children and adolescents may thus carry on to adult life two or three times the number of fat cells that normal-weight youngsters do. Children should not be encouraged to "clean their plates." Rather, they should be encouraged to eat according to appetite. Food should not be used as a reward. Nutritious foods such as fruits and vegetables should be emphasized rather than foods such as cookies or cakes that are high in calories. Finally, an example of proper nutrition and physical activity should be set by parents.

For adults, the most effective programs for weight loss typically involve decreased food consumption combined with increased physical activity.

Sedentary Lifestyle

There is accumulating evidence from large-population studies that endurance exercise exerts a protective effect against the development of coronary artery disease. It appears that moderate amounts of exercise performed regularly throughout a lifetime will have beneficial effects.

Diabetes and Glucose Intolerance

Individuals with diabetes have an increased risk for CAD. It is essential to distinguish diabetes, which occurs in 2–6% of the population, from glucose intolerance, which may occur in as much as 20%, depending on the criteria used. If you are concerned about the possibility of diabetes, and particularly if there is a history of diabetes in your family, you should see your physician for several simple blood tests which can either establish or rule out the diagnosis.

Type A Personality

There are many undefined links between the mind and the heart. In the 1960s Dr. Ray Rosenman and Dr. Meyer Friedman introduced the concept of the type A personality, who was subject to increased incidence of coronary artery disease. Subsequent studies have largely supported their contention that this cluster of personality traits is linked to increased CAD. The individual who is hard-driving and successful may or may not possess the traits of a type A personality, and the goal of eliminating all stress from life is neither realistic nor likely to lower CAD. The type A behavior pattern is characterized by some or all of the following traits: a sense of urgency, impatience, easily provoked hostility, abrupt and rapid speech, concentration on goals to the exclusion of the rest of life, high competitiveness and intense pursuit of achievement.

Positive Family History

There is no question that genetic background plays a significant role in the likelihood that an individual will develop coronary artery disease. When we talk about a positive family history for CAD, we mean that a first-degree relative (parent, sibling, child) has died of CAD or stroke before the age of 60. It is important to know if you have a positive family history since this should make you all the more vigilant to minimize your risk factors.

RISK FACTOR REDUCTION IN CHILDREN

Most people don't think about risk factors in children. After all, they think, heart attacks happen in middle-aged and older people. Yet atherosclerosis has its roots in childhood and adolescence. Lifelong habits related to food selection, amount of exercise and smoking or not smoking are often established in childhood. All parents can do their children a great service by setting a personal example of keeping risk factors under control and making sure that proper habits are established during childhood.

POSITIVE LIFESTYLE

A positive lifestyle contributes to overall health. Unfortunately, many "routine" or everyday issues are often neglected. Proper weight, emotional health, medical care and alcohol consumption, and the promotion of positive lifestyle habits in children—these are all important in maintaining overall health and well-being.

Emotional Health

The quality of individual and family emotional life is of fundamental importance. Much has been written about the high incidence of depression, anxiety, stress and substance abuse in our society. Too little attention has been focused on the positive aspects of emotional life which bring joy and fulfillment.

While we won't give you a prescription for finding happiness, there are some guidelines that seem to make sense. Dr. Jonathan Freedman, writing in his book *Happy People*, noted that happy individuals seem characterized by a deep, loving relationship with another individual. We are skeptical about programs offering "personal fulfillment" without emphasizing the importance of sharing with others. Also, happy families seem to demonstrate free and open communication among members.

Medical Care

Establishing a relationship with a physician is a very important step that you take both for yourself and your family. If you are seeking a physician it is a good idea to ask people you respect who their personal physician is. It is also a good idea to get recommendations from local hospitals, particularly ones affiliated with medical schools or residency training programs. Finally, it is very important to gauge how well you feel your doctor communicates with you. Does he or she have time to answer questions? Does he or she give you the information to participate intelligently in your own health care? With the increased knowledge available on the interaction between fitness and health, more and more physicians have become knowledgeable in this area. Use your relationship with your physician to form a partnership to help *prevent* disease, not just diagnose it. Your physician should be interested and knowledgeable in the areas of nutrition, exercise and risk factor reduction.

We believe individuals should have a thorough physical examination some time early in adulthood (preferably in the early 30s) and then once every two or three years until the age of 70, when yearly exams ought to be instituted. Of course, if you have a specific medical problem or if you develop a symptom that concerns you, it is important to see your physician.

Alcohol Consumption

Heavy drinking ranks second only to cigarette smoking as a preventable cause of death. Alcohol is involved in 40% of traffic fatalities and 25% of all hospital admissions. It has been estimated that there are between 10 and 15 million alcoholics in the United States. Heavy alcohol consumption may lead to damage to the liver and is also associated with cancers of the mouth, tongue and esophagus. Heavy drinkers also carry an increased risk of heart disease.

When it comes to alcohol, we feel that the best advice is to strike a healthy balance. While we stop short of believing that moderate alcohol consumption is a positive health benefit, it does not pose a health hazard. What constitutes a moderate amount of alcohol consumption? Most experts would agree that one 2-ounce drink of alcohol, one glass of wine or one beer a day constitutes moderate alcohol consumption.

SAFETY

A few simple steps can cut down your risks.

Seat belts: The evidence that seat belts save lives and decrease injuries is overwhelming. It is estimated that adult fatalities from motor vehicle accidents could be immediately cut in half if all passengers wore seat belts.

CPR: Cardiopulmonary resuscitation, or CPR, could save many lives if enough people learned how to perform it. Each year over a million Americans suffer heart attacks and unfortunately about half of them die—the majority before they reach the hospital. The skills involved in basic life support in CPR are easily learned. Your local hospital, branch of the American Red Cross or chapter of the American Heart Association can give you information on where classes are held in your area.

Water safety: Each year over 6,000 Americans die by drowning. Many of these deaths could be prevented with proper safety precautions and education. If you are not a strong swimmer don't go out in water above shoulder depth unless you're wearing a life jacket. Making sure that your children learn how to swim from qualified instructors is an important preventive measure. Local branches of the YMCA or the American Red Cross usually provide swimming instruction or can at least direct you to a facility where your children can learn.

First aid: Excellent first aid kits are now available commercially and no home should be without one. It is also an excellent investment of your time to take a first aid course offered by a local branch of the American Red Cross.

INDEX